Principles and Applications of Electrochemistry

Chapman and Hall Chemistry Textbook Series

CONSULTING EDITORS

R.P. Bell, M.A., Hon. L.L.D., F.R.S., Professor of Chemistry at the University of Stirling

N.N. Greenwood, Ph.D., Sc.D., Professor of Inorganic and Structural Chemistry at the University of Leeds

R.O.C. Norman, M.A., D.Sc., Professor of Chemistry at the University of York

OTHER TITLES IN THE SERIES

Symmetry in Molecules J.M. Hollas

Introduction to Molecular Photochemistry C.H.J. Wells

N.M.R. and Chemistry J.W. Akitt

The Chemistry of Non-metals P. Powell, P. Timms

Pericyclic Reactions G.B. Gill, M.R. Willis

Organometallics in Organic Synthesis J. M. Swan, D. St. C. Black

Principles and Applications of Electrochemistry

D. R. Crow

Principal Lecturer in Physical Chemistry
The Polytechnic, Wolverhampton

SECOND EDITION

LONDON
CHAPMAN AND HALL

A Halsted Press Book
John Wiley & Sons, New York

First published 1974
by Chapman and Hall Ltd
11 New Fetter Lane, London EC4P 4EE
Second edition 1979
© 1974, 1979 D.R. Crow
Printed in Great Britain by
J. W. Arrowsmith Ltd., Bristol

ISBN 0 412 16020 X

Distributed in the U.S.A. by Halsted Press,
a Division of John Wiley & Sons, Inc., New York

Library of Congress Cataloging in Publication Data

Crow, David Richard.
   Principles and applications of electrochemistry.

   (Chapman and Hall chemistry textbook series)
   'A Halsted Press book'
   1.   Electrochemistry.   I.   Title.
QD553.092   1979   541'.37   79-75
ISBN 0-470-26674-0

Contents

Preface to the first edition

The purpose of this book is to present in a simple and concise way the basic principles of electrochemistry and some of its applications.

In a volume of this size it has not been possible to give an exhaustive treatment of the subject and careful selection of material has been necessary. Despite this constraint, I have attempted to cover, in a logically developing sequence, the essential electrochemistry that students require.

Deeper insight into the subject and extended theory may be obtained from the further reading lists given at the end of each chapter. I wish to acknowledge the help that these texts and articles have been to me.

My colleagues and students have helped me greatly while writing this book; the former by their constructive criticism and advice, the latter through their questions and discussion of their problems. I cannot adequately express my gratitude to my wife for her help in typing and checking and for her encouragement and moral support.

D.R.C.
London,
April 1973

Preface to the second edition

Since the appearance of the first edition of this book in 1974, a number of people have been kind enough to point out errors and omissions and have made suggestions for improvement. I wish to acknowledge the help thus received.

The overall structure of the book remains unchanged, but certain sections have been updated in terms of units, nomenclature and the values of constants, while other sections, I trust, are improved by modification and extension.

I wish again to thank my colleagues for all their help, particularly Dr K. Miller who, in a busy life, has always found time to give assistance and advice.

Finally, I owe my greatest thanks to my wife for her continued encouragement.

D. R. C.
Wolverhampton
October 1978

The structure of electrochemistry 1

Electrochemistry is a large and important area of physical chemistry. It is, however, difficult to define precisely the limits of this area, not simply on account of its size but because of its influence in so many areas in chemistry as well as in biology and physics. Many concepts, accepted universally now as fundamental to chemistry, originated in electrochemistry. On the other hand it is now realized that future developments in many fields, and we may at random quote such widely differing ones as corrosion prevention, power supply and biochemistry and cellular biology, are dependent in no small way upon the exploitation of electrochemical principles.

In the short sections which follow an attempt is made to indicate the more important contributions that electrochemistry has made to chemistry as a whole and the important place which the subject occupies in science at the present time.

1.1 Faraday's Laws

Implicit in the demonstration and implementation of these laws are the concepts of atomic structure and the nature of ions and electrons. It is apparent that charges which are transferred through solution and across electrode/solution interfaces are 'atomic' in nature. The two laws are simply expressed as follows:

(1) In electrolytic processes the amount of chemical decomposition is proportional to the *quantity* of electricity passed.
(2) The masses of different species deposited at or dissolved from electrodes

by the same quantity of electricity are in direct proportion to $\frac{M_r}{z}\left(\text{or} \frac{A_r}{z}\right)$. M_r, A_r refer to relative molecular or atomic masses while z is the change in charge number which occurs in the electrode reaction. Thus, when a given current is passed for a given time through a series of electrolyte solutions, the extent of decomposition is always the same when expressed in terms of $\frac{1}{z}$ moles. In this statement lies the definition of the Faraday constant (F) which is the amount of electricity required to deposit $\frac{1}{z}$ mole of any species from solution and has the value 9.6487×10^4 C mol^{-1}. The units emphasize that 9.6487×10^4 coulombs is the amount of electricity associated with '1 mole of unit charges'.

1.2   Ion interactions in solution

It was appreciated very early on that in systems of oppositely charged ions in solution, independent movement of ions could not be expected except under the extreme condition of infinite dilution. Therefore, independent contribution to bulk properties such as conductance or osmotic pressure cannot occur. Electrostatics demands that considerable attractive and repulsive forces be exerted between unlike and like charges respectively. In such interactions lies, to a very large extent, the demonstrable non-ideal behaviour of electrolyte solutions.

Debye and Hückel rationalized the way in which the conductivities of strong electrolyte solutions were observed to vary with their concentration by proposing models of the ion distribution and applying to them well-established relationships of thermodynamics and electrostatics. The concept of ion atmospheres, formed by the preferential distribution of ions about a given central ion carrying charge of opposite sign, when developed in this way, provided experimentally verifiable expressions for the mean ion activity coefficients of electrolytes. These expressions make possible the determination of thermodynamic equilibrium constants in electrolyte systems and the interpretation of ionic reaction rates in solution.

1.3   Acid–base theory

The classical theory of electrolytic dissociation put forward by Arrhenius is successful in explaining to a large extent the behaviour of weak acids and bases in aqueous solution. It led to the concept of pH and pH scale of acidity for aqueous solutions. The realization that the solvent plays a vital role in ionic equilibria led to the development of a general theory of acids and bases applicable to *all* solvents.

1.4   Thermodynamics

Much of conventional thermodynamics developed from electrochemical work. The detailed investigation of the behaviour of reversible electrochemical cells and the reactions occurring within them contributed to the appreciation of the concept of standard free energy and led to the accurate determination of thermodynamic constants for cell reactions. Early work on the temperature dependence of reversible cell e.m.f.'s contributed considerably to the formulation of the Third Law of Thermodynamics.

It is, in fact, with the use and understanding of reversible electrochemical cells that many people see for the first time the significance and applicability of thermodynamic principles. Here thermodynamics may be seen to apply to tangible practical situations.

So many modern analytical techniques are based upon electrochemistry. Quite apart from *methods* based on the direct measurement of a current, voltage or resistance, classical 'wet' analysis stands on the electrochemical foundation of equilibria and electrode potentials.

1.5   Interfacial phenomena

The interfacial region between a solid electrode surface and a solution with which it is in contact is of great significance. An understanding of the structure of this region is necessary to explain the mechanisms and rates of oxidation–reduction processes occurring at the electrode. The theory of this 'double-layer' region lies at the heart of the physical chemistry of colloid systems and the interpretation of colloid stability, membrane behaviour and ion-exchange processes lie within the realm of interfacial electrochemistry.

1.6   Electrode processes

Studies grouped under this general heading are concerned with the kinetics and mechanisms of electrode reactions. They are to be distinguished from thermodynamic studies, based upon reversible cells and electrode potentials in which, by definition, systems at equilibrium are investigated.

Detailed knowledge of the energetics and kinetics of electrode processes and the factors which affect them, is essential for the efficient running of the electroplating, electroforming and electromachining industries. Corrosion mechanisms and the control of corrosion can only be interpreted quantitatively in terms of electrode kinetics. The development of understanding of electrode processes is reflected in the increased utilization of electrochemical processes as sources of energy – both in storage and power generating devices. Such utilization is likely to increase dramatically over the next few decades with the increasing demand for non-polluting energy production.

1.7   The domains of electrochemistry

It can be seen from the previous sections what a range of chemical disciplines have their roots in electrochemistry. This emphasizes the necessity for *every* chemist to have a sound grasp of electrochemical principles. Indeed, many modern developments in molecular biology stress the electrochemical basis of many natural processes, e.g. nerve response by conduction of electricity, the pH dependence of amino acid and protein equilibria, cell membrane equilibria and ion-body fluid redox equilibria. It is becoming more apparent that an electrochemical background is essential for biologists.

It is hardly surprising that, since electrochemistry makes incursions into so much of chemistry, opinions as to what constitutes the subject are numerous. While the classification of such areas as electroplating, storage batteries and fuel cells as 'electrochemistry' would be almost universally accepted, the position of some other areas could call forth considerable disagreement.

If the widest view is taken of the material considered above, and this is only generally expressed and not exhaustive, it is apparent that there are essentially *three* domains of electrochemistry which may be expressed in tabular form.

4

Ionics	Interfacial phenomena	Electrodics
Behaviour of ions in solution and in fused state	Double layer theory	Kinetics and mechanisms of electrode reactions
	Adsorption	
Ionic equilibria	Electrokinetic phenomena	Electron transfer reactions
Transport processes	Colloidal systems	Electro-catalytic processes
Potential-determining ion reactions (reversible electrode potentials)	Ion exchange processes	

Strictly, it is necessary to include a further domain which takes its place to the right of electrodics above. This is the solid state physics of the electrode materials used and is concerned essentially with the structure of the materials used as electrodes and the energy levels of electrons and atoms within them.

Owing to the size of the subject, it has proved necessary in the following chapters, to be selective in the choice of material presented. Earlier chapters are concerned with ionics and its applications. Here are considered ion interactions in solution, acid–base equilibria, transport phenomena, and the concept of reversible electrode potential. This last named leads to the development of reversible cells and their exploitation. Here one is dealing with electrochemical thermodynamics – with the rapid attainment of equilibrium between species at an electrode surface and charged species in solution.

Chapter 7, devoted to interfacial phenomena, deals with the theory of the double layer at electrode/solution interfaces but develops the concept in the treatment of electrokinetic phenomena, colloidal systems and membrane equilibria. It forms a bridge between the earlier part of the book and the section concerned with electrodics with which it concludes.

Ionic interaction 2

2.1   The nature of electrolytes

Electrolytes are species giving rise to ions to a greater or lesser extent; strong electrolytes being completely ionized even in the solid and fused states. In the latter case, and also when dissolved in a solvent, the ions become free to move and the highly ordered lattice structure characteristic of crystals is almost entirely destroyed. Weak electrolytes, on the other hand, are ionized to only a small extent in solution; ionization increasing with dilution according to the well-known Ostwald Law.

Very many salts are known to dissolve readily in solvents with heats of solution that are usually fairly small in magnitude and which may be exothermic or endothermic. At first sight this is rather a difficult phenomenon to account for, since crystal structures have high *lattice energies.* A lattice energy is the large-scale analogue of the dissociation energy of an individual ionic 'molecule'. In a crystal, the energies of a large number of component ion-pairs contribute to the total lattice energy which is effectively the energy evolved when the lattice is built up from free ions. Since such energies are large, we are led to suppose that a large amount of energy is required to break down the ordered structure and liberate free ions. A way in which the observed easy dissolution can be explained is by the simultaneous occurrence of another process which produces sufficient energy to compensate for that lost in the rupture of the lattice bonds. Exothermic reactions of individual ions with the solvent – giving rise to the heat of solvation – provide the necessary energy. From the First Law of Thermodynamics, the algebraic sum of the lattice and solvation energies is the heat of solution. This explains both why the heats of solution are usually fairly small and why they may be endothermic or exothermic – depending upon whether the lattice energy or solvation energy is the greater quantity.

A great difficulty when dealing with electrolytes is to ascribe individual properties to individual ions. Individual thermodynamic properties cannot be determined, only mean ion quantities being measurable. Interionic and ion–solvent interactions are so numerous and important in solution that, except in the most dilute cases, no ion may be regarded as behaving independently of others. On the other hand, there is no doubt that certain dynamic properties such as ion conductances, mobilities and transport numbers may be determined, although values for such properties are not absolute but vary with ion environment.

2.2   Ion activity

Since the properties of one ion species are affected by the presence of other ions with which it interacts electrostatically, except at infinite dilution, the concentration of a species is an unsatisfactory parameter to use in attempting to predict its contribution to the bulk properties of a solution. What is rather required is a parameter similar to, and indeed related to, concentration, i.e. the actual number of ions present, but which expresses the *availability* of the species to determine properties, to take part in a chemical reaction or to influence the position of an equilibrium. This parameter is known as *activity* (*a*) and is related to concentration (*c*) by the simple relationship

$$a_i = \gamma_i c_i \qquad (2.1)$$

γ_i is known as an activity coefficient which may take different forms depending on the way in which concentrations for a given system are expressed, i.e. as molarity, molality or mole fraction. For instance, the chemical potential (μ_i) of a species i may be expressed in the forms

$$\mu_i = (\mu_i^{\ominus})_x + RT \ln x_i \gamma_x \qquad (2.2a)$$

$$\mu_i = (\mu_i^{\ominus})_c + RT \ln c_i \gamma_c \qquad (2.2b)$$

$$\mu_i = (\mu_i^{\ominus})_m + RT \ln m_i \gamma_m \qquad (2.2c)$$

x_i, c_i and m_i are the mole fraction, molar concentration and molal concentration respectively. γ_x is known as the *rational activity coefficient* while γ_c, γ_m are *practical activity coefficients*. (Often, the symbols f_x, f_c are used for molar and molal activity coefficients, but to avoid confusion γ will be used throughout with an appropriate suffix to indicate the concentration units.)

Until about 1923 activity coefficients were purely empirical quantities in that when concentrations were modified by their use, correct results could be predicted for the properties of a system. We shall see that, on the basis of the Debye–Hückel theory, to be discussed shortly, activity coefficients become rationalized and theoretically predictable quantities.

For the purposes of deriving relationships in which activity coefficients occur it is very convenient to make use of the idea of individual ion activities and activity coefficients. However, as already stressed, such quantities are incapable of *measurement* and so are meaningless in a *practical* sense. One ion species, deriving from a dissolved electrolyte, cannot on its own determine properties of a system; it will always do so in concert with an equivalent number of oppositely charged ions. It is therefore only possible to use a form of activity or activity coefficient which takes account of both types of ions characteristic of an electrolyte. Such forms are known as mean ion activities ($a_\pm$) and mean ion activity coefficients ($\gamma_\pm$) and are defined by

$$(a_\pm)^\nu = a_+^{\nu_+} \times a_-^{\nu_-} \qquad (2.3)$$

and

$$(\gamma_\pm)^\nu = \gamma_+^{\nu_+} \times \gamma_-^{\nu_-} \qquad (2.4)$$

where $\nu = \nu_+ + \nu_-$, the latter being the number of cations and anions respectively deriving from each formula unit of the electrolyte.

2.3   Ion–ion and ion–solvent interactions

Although strong electrolytes are completely ionized, their ions are not entirely free to move independently of one another through the body of a solution, except when this is infinitely dilute. A fairly realistic picture of the situation in a solution containing the oppositely charged ions of an electrolyte is as follows. Ions will move randomly with respect to one another due to fairly violent thermal motion. Even in this condition, however, coulombic forces will exert their influence to some extent with the result that each cation and anion is surrounded on a time average by an 'ion atmosphere' containing a relatively higher proportion of ions carrying charge of an opposite sign to that on the central ion.

Movement of ions under the influence of an applied field will be very slow and subject to disruption by the thermal motion. Under the influence of such a field, movement of the atmosphere occurs in a direction opposite to that of the central ion, resulting in the continuous breakdown and re-formation of the atmosphere as the ion moves in one direction through the solution. The time-lag between the restructuring of the atmosphere and the movement of the central ion causes the atmosphere to be asymmetrically distributed around the central ion causing some attraction of the latter in a direction opposite to that of its motion. This is known as the *asymmetry*, or *relaxation effect*. In addition, central ions experience increased viscous hindrance to their motion on account of solvated atmosphere ions which, on account of the latter's movement in the opposite direction to the central ion, produce movement of solvent in this opposing direction as well. This is known as the *electrophoretic effect*.

Such interactions must obviously increase in significance with increasing concentration of the electrolyte. In the extreme condition of infinite dilution, all interionic effects are eliminated, ions move without the above restrictions, current may pass freely and consequently conductivity reaches a maximum value – a result, as we shall see shortly, in accordance with experience. In another extreme situation, interionic attraction may become so great that the formation of discreet *ion-pairs* may be regarded as occurring. The most favourable conditions for such behaviour are high electrolyte concentration and high valency of the ions. It is therefore seen to be important to distinguish between complete *ionization* and complete *dissociation*. Ion-pairs consist of *associated* ions, the formation of which must be regarded as a time-averaged situation since in any such system there will be a continual interchange of ions amongst the pairs. For a species to be regarded as an ion-pair it must be a 'kinetically distinct' species. That is, although it is an unstable and transient entity, it nevertheless has a lifetime of such duration that it can experience a number of kinetic collisions before exchanging an ion partner.

2.4 The electrical potential in the vicinity of an ion

By definition, the electrical potential, ψ, at some point is the work done in bringing a unit positive charge from infinity (where $\psi = 0$) to that point (Fig. 2.1).

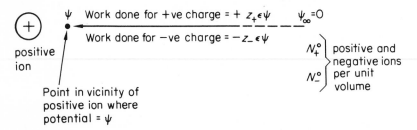

FIGURE 2.1
The work of bringing charges from infinity ($\psi_\infty = 0$) to a point near a selected ion where the potential = ψ.

The concentration of positive and negative ions (N_+, N_-) at the point where the potential is ψ may be found from the Boltzmann distribution law, thus

$$N_+ = N_+{}^0 \, e^{-(z_+\epsilon\psi/kT)}$$

and

$$N_- = N_-{}^0 \, e^{+(z_-\epsilon\psi/kT)} \tag{2.5}$$

where ϵ is the unit electronic charge, k the Boltzmann constant, z_+, z_- the number of charges carried by positive and negative ions respectively, and N_+^0, N_-^0 the number of ions of each type per unit volume in the bulk.

It is seen that these equations are consistent with the expected fact that there are, on average, more negative ions than positive ions in the vicinity of a given positive ion and vice versa.

The electrical density (ρ) at the point where the potential is ψ is the excess positive or negative electricity per unit volume at that point. It is easily seen that for the present case this must be

$$\rho = N_+z_+\epsilon - N_-z_-\epsilon$$
$$= N_+{}^0z_+\epsilon \, e^{-(z_+\epsilon\psi/kT)} - N_-{}^0z_-\epsilon \, e^{+(z_-\epsilon\psi/kT)} \tag{2.6}$$

For the simplest case of a $1:1$ electrolyte

$$z_+ = z_- \ \ = 1$$

and

$$N_+{}^0 = N_-{}^0 = N_i$$

i.e.

$$\rho = N_i \epsilon [e^{-\epsilon\psi/kT} - e^{\epsilon\psi/kT}] \tag{2.7}$$

If it is assumed that $\epsilon\psi/kT \ll 1$, the two exponential terms may be expanded and all but the first terms in the expansions neglected so that Equation (2.7) becomes

$$\rho \sim -2N_i \left[\frac{\epsilon^2 \psi}{kT}\right] \tag{2.8}$$

For the more general case where $z_+, z_- \neq 1$, Equation (2.8) becomes modified to

$$\rho \sim -\Sigma N_i z_i{}^2 \left[\frac{\epsilon^2 \psi}{kT}\right] \tag{2.9}$$

The electrostatic potential and charge density are also related in the Poisson equation, viz.

$$\frac{\partial^2 \psi}{\partial x^2} + \frac{\partial^2 \psi}{\partial y^2} + \frac{\partial^2 \psi}{\partial z^2} = -\frac{\rho}{\varepsilon_0 \varepsilon} \tag{2.10}$$

where ε_0 is the *permittivity* of a vacuum ($8\cdot854 \times 10^{-12}\,C^2\ N^{-1}\ m^{-2}$) and ε is the *relative permittivity*, or dielectric constant, of the solvent. x, y, z are the rectangular coordinates of the point at which the potential is ψ. In terms of polar coordinates Equation (2.10) becomes

$$\frac{1}{r^2}\frac{\partial}{\partial r}\left(r^2 \frac{\partial\psi}{\partial r}\right) = -\frac{\rho}{\varepsilon_0 \varepsilon} \tag{2.11}$$

Substituting for ρ from Equation (2.9) we have that

$$\frac{1}{r^2}\frac{\partial}{\partial r}\left(r^2 \frac{\partial\psi}{\partial r}\right) = \frac{\epsilon^2 \psi}{\varepsilon_0 \varepsilon kT}\Sigma N_i z_i{}^2 \tag{2.12}$$

which we will express as $\kappa^2\psi$

11

where
$$\kappa = \left[\frac{e^2 \Sigma N_i z_i^2}{\varepsilon_0 \varepsilon k T}\right]^{1/2} \tag{2.13}$$

A general solution of Equation (2.12) takes the form

$$\psi = \frac{A\,e^{-\kappa r}}{r} + \frac{A'\,e^{\kappa r}}{r} \tag{2.14}$$

in which A, A' are integration constants. The second term may, in fact, be ignored, since as $r \to \infty$, $\psi \to 0$, thus A' must be zero, i.e. ψ must be *finite* even for very large values of r.

Thus,
$$\psi = \frac{A\,e^{-\kappa r}}{r} \tag{2.15}$$

and since
$$\kappa^2 \psi = -\frac{\rho}{\varepsilon_0 \varepsilon}$$

substitution of ψ from Equation (2.15) into the expression

$$\rho = -\kappa^2 \psi \varepsilon_0 \varepsilon$$

yields
$$\rho = - A\,\frac{\kappa^2 \varepsilon_0 \varepsilon}{r} \cdot e^{-\kappa r} \tag{2.16}$$

For electro-neutrality, the total negative charge of the atmosphere about a given positively charged central ion is $-z_i e$. The total charge of the atmo-

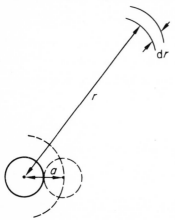

FIGURE 2.2
Model for calculation of charge of an ion atmosphere about a central ion.

sphere is determined by considering the charge carried by a spherical shell of thickness dr and distance r from the central ion and integrating from the closest distance that atmosphere and central ions may approach out to infinity (Fig 2.2)

Thus

$$\int_a^\infty 4\pi r^2 \rho \, dr = -z_i \epsilon \tag{2.17}$$

Therefore,

$$A\kappa^2 \varepsilon_0 \varepsilon \int_a^\infty 4\pi r e^{-\kappa r} \, dr = z_i \epsilon \tag{2.18}$$

Integration by parts gives A as

$$A = \frac{z_i \epsilon}{4\pi\varepsilon_0 \varepsilon} \cdot \frac{e^{\kappa a}}{1 + \kappa a} \tag{2.19}$$

So that the potential ψ may now be expressed by

$$\psi = \frac{z_i \epsilon}{4\pi\varepsilon_0 \varepsilon} \cdot \frac{e^{\kappa a}}{1 + \kappa a} \cdot \frac{e^{-\kappa r}}{r} \tag{2.20}$$

When r approaches a, the distance of closest approach, Equation (2.20) becomes

$$\psi = \frac{z_i \epsilon}{4\pi\varepsilon_0 \varepsilon a} \cdot \frac{1}{1 + \kappa a} = \frac{z_i \epsilon}{4\pi\varepsilon_0 \varepsilon a} - \frac{z_i \epsilon}{4\pi\varepsilon_0 \varepsilon} \cdot \frac{\kappa}{1 + \kappa a} \tag{2.21}$$

or, in the most general terms

$$\psi = \pm \frac{z_i \epsilon}{4\pi\varepsilon_0 \varepsilon a} \mp \frac{z_i \epsilon}{4\pi\varepsilon_0 \varepsilon} \cdot \frac{\kappa}{1 + \kappa a} \tag{2.22}$$

It is now clear that ψ is composed of two contributions, one due to the ion itself

$$\frac{z_i \epsilon}{4\pi\varepsilon_0 \varepsilon a}$$

and the other given by

$$\frac{z_i \epsilon}{4\pi\varepsilon_0 \varepsilon} \cdot \frac{\kappa}{1 + \kappa a}$$

This latter term represents the potential on the ion due to its atmosphere. We are now able to have some physical picture of the significance of κ. The expression

$$\frac{\kappa}{1 + \kappa a}$$

in the second term on the right-hand side of Equation (2.22) corresponds to $1/a$ in the first term, i.e.

$$\frac{1 + \kappa a}{\kappa}$$

is an effective radius – that of the ion atmosphere.

2.5 Electrical potential and thermodynamic functions. The Debye–Hückel equation

.The chemical potential μ_i of an ion i in an ideal solution is given by

$$\mu_i = \mu_i^{\ominus} + RT \ln x_i \qquad (2.23)$$

x_i being the mole fraction of ion i.

For non-ideal solutions Equation (2.23) must be modified in terms of the activity of i rather than its mole fraction, thus

$$\mu_i = \mu_i^{\ominus} + RT \ln x_i + RT \ln \gamma_i \qquad (2.24)$$

By definition μ_i is the change in free energy of the system which would occur if 1 mole of species i were added to a large quantity of it. The term $RT \ln \gamma_i$ in Equation (2.24) may be regarded as the contribution that the ion atmosphere makes to the total energy of the ion. The contribution per ion is $kT \ln \gamma_i$ and may be equated to the work which must be performed to give an ion of potential ψ_i (due to its atmosphere) its charge $z_i \epsilon$.

The work done, dw, in charging the ion by an increment of charge, $d\epsilon$, is given by

$$dw = \psi_i \, d\epsilon \qquad (2.25)$$

so that the work, w, required to give the ion its charge $z_i\epsilon$ is

$$w = \int_0^{z_i\epsilon} \psi_i \, d\epsilon$$

$$= -\int_0^{z_i\epsilon} \frac{z_i\epsilon}{4\pi\varepsilon_0\,\varepsilon} \cdot \frac{\kappa}{1+\kappa a} \, d\epsilon \tag{2.26}$$

$$= -\frac{z_i^2\,\epsilon^2\kappa}{8\pi\varepsilon_0\,\varepsilon\,(1+\kappa a)} \tag{2.27}$$

Therefore,

$$kT \ln \gamma_i = -\frac{z_i^2\,\epsilon^2}{8\pi\varepsilon_0\,\varepsilon} \cdot \frac{\kappa}{1+\kappa a} \tag{2.28}$$

Equation (2.28) gives the individual activity coefficient of the i-type ion which has no practical significance. In terms of the mean ion activity coefficient for the electrolyte Equation (2.28) becomes

$$\ln \gamma_\pm = -\frac{\epsilon^2}{8\pi\varepsilon_0\,\varepsilon kT}\,|z_+z_-|\,\frac{\kappa}{1+\kappa a} \tag{2.29}$$

Now

$$\kappa = \left[\frac{\epsilon^2}{\varepsilon_0\varepsilon kT}\,\Sigma N_i z_i^2\right]^{1/2} \qquad \text{(see Equation (2.13))}$$

in which $N_i = NC_i$, where N is the Avogadro constant and C_i is the ion concentration in mol m^{-3}.

Thus,

$$\kappa = \left(\frac{\epsilon^2 N}{\varepsilon_0\,\varepsilon kT} \cdot \Sigma C_i z_i^2\right)^{1/2}$$

or

$$\kappa = \left(\frac{2\epsilon^2 N}{\varepsilon_0\,\varepsilon kT} \cdot \tfrac{1}{2}\,\Sigma C_i z_i^2\right)^{1/2} \tag{2.30}$$

It is seen that Equation (2.30) contains the expression $\tfrac{1}{2}\Sigma C_i z_i^2$. This is very similar in form to the expression defining the *ionic strength*, I, of the solution, viz.

$$I = \tfrac{1}{2}\,\Sigma m_i z_i^2 \tag{2.31}$$

15

where m_i represents the concentration of each ion of the electrolyte in the units mol kg^{-1}.

Now, if C_i in mol m^{-3}, as used above, is replaced by c_i in mol dm^{-3}, then $N_i = 10^3 Nc_i$, and if the solution is of such dilution that 1 dm^3 corresponds closely to 1 dm^3 of pure solvent, i.e. 1 kg for the case of water, we may write

$$N_i = 10^3 Nm_i$$

Thus Equation (2.30) becomes

$$\kappa = \left(\frac{2 \times 10^3 \ \epsilon^2 N}{\varepsilon_0 \ \varepsilon kT} \cdot \tfrac{1}{2} \Sigma m_i z_i^2 \right)^{\tfrac{1}{2}}$$

or

$$\kappa = \left(\frac{2 \times 10^3 \ \epsilon^2 N}{\varepsilon_0 \ \varepsilon kT} \right)^{\tfrac{1}{2}} \sqrt{I} \tag{2.32}$$

This expression for κ may now be substituted into Equation (2.29) to give, after conversion to logarithms to base 10,

$$\log \gamma_\pm = - \frac{\epsilon^2 N}{2 \cdot 303 \times 8\pi \ \varepsilon_0 \varepsilon RT} | z_+ z_- | \frac{\left(\dfrac{2 \times 10^3 \ \epsilon^2 \ N^2}{\varepsilon_0 \ \varepsilon RT} \right)^{\tfrac{1}{2}} \sqrt{I}}{1 + \left(\dfrac{2 \times 10^3 \ \epsilon^2 \ N^2}{\varepsilon_0 \varepsilon RT} \right)^{\tfrac{1}{2}} a\sqrt{I}}$$

(Noting that $k = R/N$). $\tag{2.33}$

Or, more simply, in a form which collects constants,

$$-\log \gamma_\pm = \frac{| z_+ z_- | A\sqrt{I}}{1 + Ba\sqrt{I}} \tag{2.34}$$

This is the Debye–Hückel equation in which A and B are seen to be constants for a particular solvent at a given temperature and pressure, viz.

$$A = \frac{\epsilon^2 N}{2 \cdot 303 \ RT \times 8\pi \ \varepsilon_0 \ \varepsilon} \left(\frac{2 \times 10^3 \ N^2 \ \epsilon^2}{\varepsilon_0 \varepsilon RT} \right)^{\tfrac{1}{2}} \tag{2.35}$$

$$B = \left(\frac{2 \times 10^3 \ N^2 \ \epsilon^2}{\varepsilon_0 \ \varepsilon RT} \right)^{\tfrac{1}{2}} \tag{2.36}$$

The above constants may be calculated for water at 298 K by substitution of the data.

$$\epsilon = 1\cdot6021 \times 10^{-19} \text{ As}; N = 6\cdot023 \times 10^{23} \text{ mol}^{-1};$$

$$\varepsilon_0 = 8\cdot8542 \times 10^{-12} \text{ kg}^{-1} \text{ m}^{-3} \text{ s}^4 \text{ A}^2; \varepsilon = 78\cdot54;$$

$$R = 8\cdot314 \text{ J K}^{-1} \text{ mol}^{-1}; T = 298 \text{ K}.$$

Thus

$$A = 0\cdot507 \text{ mol}^{-\frac{1}{2}} \text{ kg}^{\frac{1}{2}}$$

$$B = 3\cdot290 \times 10^9 \text{ m}^{-1} \text{ mol}^{-\frac{1}{2}} \text{kg}^{\frac{1}{2}} .$$

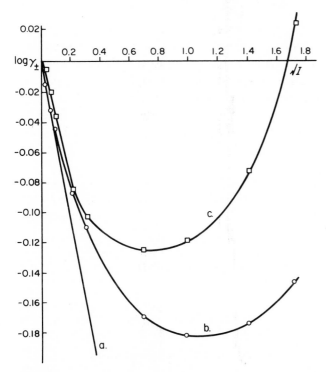

FIGURE 2.3
Variation of mean ion activity coefficients with ionic strength ($\log \gamma_\pm$ versus $\sqrt{I}$).

(a) Limiting Law line for 1 : 1 electrolyte.
(b) Experimental graph for NaCl.
(c) Experimental graph for KOH.

17

2.6 Limiting and extended forms of the Debye–Hückel equation

For very dilute solutions the denominator of Equation (2.34) is very little different from unity, bearing in mind that a is of the order of 10^{-8} cm. Thus, for such conditions, the so-called 'Limiting Law' holds, viz.

$$- \log \gamma_{\pm} = |z_+ z_-| A \sqrt{I} \tag{2.37}$$

Equation (2.34) may be rearranged to the following

$$-\frac{A|z_+ z_-| \sqrt{I}}{\log \gamma_{\pm}} = 1 + Ba \sqrt{I} \tag{2.38}$$

The left-hand side of Equation (2.38) may be determined experimentally under conditions where the limiting law holds. Then, if B for the solvent is known, the left-hand side of the equation may be plotted as a function of $\sqrt{I}$ to give a value of the distance of closest approach, a, from the slope of the graph. Here a drawback is encountered since very often the values obtained for a are physically meaningless in that they are far too small or even negative. Nevertheless, with the assumption of a reasonable magnitude for a (~ 0.4 nm). Equation (2.34) does hold for many electrolytes up to $I \sim 0.1$.

In practice activity coefficients initially decrease with increasing concentration of electrolyte (Fig. 2.3). Such behaviour is entirely consistent with both the Debye–Hückel equation and its limiting form. However, in practice, activity coefficients show a turning point at some value of I, after which they progressively increase. It is thus seen to be necessary to modify Equation (2.34) by the addition of a further term which is an increasing function of I, i.e.,

$$\log \gamma_{\pm} -\frac{A|z_+ z_-| \sqrt{I}}{1 + Ba \sqrt{I}} + bI \tag{2.39}$$

This last relationship has become known as the Hückel equation.

2.7 Applications of the Debye–Hückel equation

The various forms of the equations resulting from the Debye–Hückel theory find practical application in the determination of activity coefficients and make possible the determination of thermodynamic data. Two important cases will be considered here.

2.7.1 Determination of thermodynamic equilibrium constants

Let us consider as an example the dissociation of a 1 : 1 weak electrolyte AB

$$AB \rightleftharpoons A^+ + B^-$$

The thermodynamic dissociation constant K_T is given by

$$K_T = \frac{[A^+][B^-]}{[AB]} \frac{\gamma_{A^+} \gamma_{B^-}}{\gamma_{AB}}$$

$$= K \frac{\gamma_\pm^2}{\gamma_{AB}}$$

$$K_T \sim K\gamma_\pm^2 \qquad (2.40)$$

where K is the concentration, or conditional dissociation constant. For a weak electrolyte in dilute solution γ_{AB} for the undissociated, and therefore non-ionic, species is very nearly unity. Taking logarithms of Equation (2.40) and substituting for $\gamma_\pm$ from the limiting law expression, we obtain

$$\log K = \log K_T + 2A\sqrt{I} \qquad (2.41)$$

K_T may therefore be determined from measured values of K over a range of ionic strength values and extrapolating the K versus $\sqrt{I}$ plot to $\sqrt{I} = 0$. This is a general technique for the determination of all types of thermodynamic equilibrium constants, e.g., solubility, stability and acid dissociation constants.

2.7.2 Effect of ionic strength on ion reaction rates in solution

In the treatment of ionic reactions by Brønsted and Bjerrum an equilibrium is considered to exist between reactant ions and a 'critical complex', the latter bearing close resemblance to the activated complex of the theory of absolute reaction rates. Thus, for the reaction scheme

$$A^{z_A} + B^{z_B} \rightleftharpoons (x^{(z_A + z_B)})^{\ddagger} \rightarrow products \qquad (2.42)$$

19

we may write, for the pre-equilibrium

$$K = \frac{[x^{\ddagger}]}{[A][B]} \frac{\gamma_{\ddagger}}{\gamma_A \gamma_B} \qquad (2.43)$$

(omitting charges for clarity) so that the rate, v, with which A and B react may be expressed by

$$v = k[A][B] = k_0[A][B] \frac{\gamma_A \gamma_B}{\gamma_{\ddagger}} \qquad (2.44)$$

where

$$k = k_0 \frac{\gamma_A \gamma_B}{\gamma_{\ddagger}} \qquad (2.45)$$

k_0, k being the rate constants at infinite and finite dilution, respectively. In logarithmic form Equation (2.45) becomes

$$\log k = \log k_0 + \log \gamma_A + \log \gamma_B - \log \gamma_{\ddagger} \qquad (2.46)$$

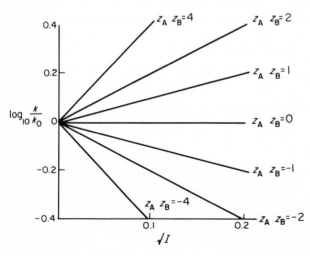

FIGURE 2.4
Theoretical variations of rate with $\sqrt{I}$ for reactions showing different values of the product z_A

in which activity coefficients may be expressed by Equation (2.34) thus,

$$\log k = \log k_0 - \frac{A\sqrt{I}}{1 + Ba\sqrt{I}} [z_A^2 + z_B^2 - (z_A + z_B)^2]$$

$$\therefore \log k = \log k_0 + \frac{2Az_A z_B \sqrt{I}}{1 + Ba\sqrt{I}} \tag{2.47}$$

or,

$$\log k \sim \log k_0 + 2Az_A z_B \sqrt{I} \tag{2.48}$$

in very dilute solution, or,

$$\log k \sim \log k_0 + 1.02 z_A z_B \sqrt{I} \tag{2.49}$$

for water as solvent at 298 K.

These last equations take account of the salt effect observed for reactions between ions, the slopes of graphs of $\log k/k_0$ versus $\sqrt{I}$ being very close to those predicted by Equation (2.49) at low concentrations (Fig. 2.4). At higher concentrations, deviations from linearity occur and these are particularly noticeable for reactions having $z_A z_B = 0$, e.g. for a reaction between an ion and a neutral molecule. According to Equation (2.49) such reactions should show no variation of rate with ionic strength and this is indeed the case up until about $I = 0.1$. Above this point, increasing ionic strength does cause the rate to vary. The reason for this is the bI term of the Hückel equation (2.39). In this case it may be readily shown that

$$\log k = \log k_0 + (b_A + b_B - b_{\ddagger})I \tag{2.50}$$

so that $\log k/k_0$ in this case becomes a linear function of I rather than of $\sqrt{I}$. This has been experimentally verified.

2.8   Ion association

It is found that in many cases experimental values of conductances do not agree with theoretical values predicted by the Onsager equation (see Equation (4.20)) and that mean ion activity coefficients cannot always be properly predicted by the Debye–Hückel theory. It was suggested by Bjerrum that, under certain conditions, oppositely charged ions of an electrolyte can associate to form ion pairs. In some circumstances, even association to the extent of forming triple or quadruple ions may occur. The most favourable situation for association is for smaller ions with high charges in solvents of low dielectric constant. Hence such phenomena occur to a usually small extent in water.

Association leads to a smaller number of particles in a system and associated species have a lower charge than non-associated ones. This will obviously serve to diminish the magnitudes of properties of a solution which are dependent on the number of solute particles and the charges carried by them.

Bjerrum's basic assumption was that the Debye–Hückel theory holds so

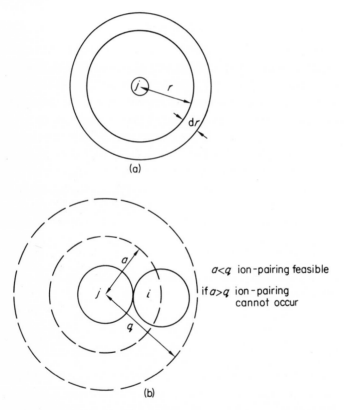

FIGURE 2.5
(a) Model for determination of distribution of i-ions within shells of specified dimensions about j-ions.
(b) Relation of a to q for ion pairing.

long as the oppositely charged ions of an electrolyte are separated by a distance q *greater* than a certain minimum value given by

$$q = \frac{z_i z_j e^2}{8\pi \varepsilon_0 \varepsilon kT} \qquad (2.51)$$

When the ion separation is less than q, ion pairing is regarded as taking place. Equation (2.51) may be derived from a consideration of the Boltzmann distribution of i-type ions in a thin shell of thickness dr at a distance r from a central j-type ion (Fig. 2.5).

The number of i-type ions in such a shell is given by

$$dN_i = N_i \exp\left[\pm \frac{z_i e \psi_j}{kT}\right] 4\pi r^2 \, dr \qquad (2.52)$$

The potential at a *small* distance from the central j-ion may be assumed to arise almost entirely from that ion and is given by Equation (2.22) as

$$\psi_j = \pm \frac{z_j e}{4\pi \varepsilon_0 \varepsilon r} \qquad (2.53)$$

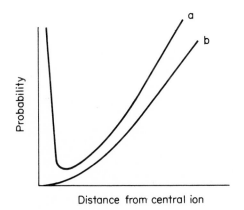

FIGURE 2.6
Shapes of probability curves for distribution of (a) i-ions about j-ions; (b) j-ions about j-ions.

23

Thus,

$$dN_i = 4\pi N_i \exp\left(-\frac{z_i z_j \epsilon^2}{4\pi \varepsilon_0 \varepsilon\, kTr}\right) r^2 \; dr \qquad (2.54)$$

One expects to find decreasing probability of finding i-type ions per unit volume at increasing values of r. However, the volumes of the concentric shells increase outwards from a j-ion so that, in fact, the probability passes through a minimum at some critical distance. A plot of calculated probability versus r shows such a minimum (Fig. 2.6).

It may be seen from the minimum condition, $dN_i/dr = 0$, that this distance is given by Equation (2.51).

For a 1:1 electrolyte in aqueous solution at 298 K, q has the value 0·357 nm. Should the sum of the respective ionic radii be less than this figure then ion pair formation will be favoured.

It is evident that for a given electrolyte at constant temperature, lowering of dielectric constant will encourage association. For tetraisoamylammonium nitrate the sum of ion radii is of the order of 0·7 nm. This gives a value of about 42 for ε by substitution into Equation (2.51) and implies that, for solvents of greater dielectric constant than 42, there should be no association but rather complete dissociation, i.e., the Debye–Hückel theory should hold good. Conductance measurements have verified that, in fact, virtually all ion pairing has ceased for $\varepsilon > 42$.

Further reading

Davies, C.W. (1962), *Ion Association*, Butterworths, London.
Harned, H.S., and Owen, B.B. (1958), *The Physical Chemistry of Electrolytic Solutions*, 3rd Edn., Reinhold, New York.
Monk, C.B. (1961), *Electrolytic Dissociation*, Academic Press, London and New York.
Prue, J.E. (1966), *Ionic Equilibria*, Pergamon Press, Oxford.
Robinson, R.A., and Stokes, R.H. (1959), *Electrolyte Solutions*, 2nd Edn. Butterworths, London.
Nancollas, G.H. (1966), *Interactions in Electrolyte Solutions*, Elsevier, Amsterdam.

Ionic equilibria and acid-base theory

3

3.1   Classical theory

Arrhenius put forward the idea of incomplete dissociation of weak electrolytes on the basis of observed anomalies in the values of colligative properties for electrolytes. Thus, the depression of freezing point of water containing a non-electrolyte is less than that with the same molar proportion of a weak electrolyte. Except at very high dilutions, however, the depression does not approach that to be expected for the total number of ions to which the complete dissociation of the electrolyte gives rise. The classical dissociation theory, concerned essentially with aqueous solutions, rests on the concept of incomplete dissociation of weak electrolytes which increases with dilution. The Arrhenius theory considers the parent electrolyte and ions produced from it as behaving in their own right, any chemical interaction with the solvent molecules being ignored, the solvent being simply regarded as a medium within which dissociation and dispersal of ions may occur.

The Arrhenius theory similarly attempts to define acids and bases as isolated species in solution giving rise, respectively, to hydrogen ions and hydroxide ions. While this view accounts for some properties of acids and bases and their reactions, it cannot begin to explain acidic and basic characteristics in non-aqueous media. Acidic and basic properties are, in fact, *consequent upon* interaction with the solvent and until such interaction has taken place the properties are not shown.

Despite the shortcomings of the classical theory, the relations derived from its use do allow the calculation of reliable equilibrium data for weak electrolytes, including acids and bases, in aqueous solution. Consider a solution of a binary electrolyte, BA, at a concentration, C mol dm^{-3}. If only a fraction α, of

BA ionizes, there will result an equilibrium mixture of $C(1 - \alpha)$ mol dm^{-3} of BA in company with $C\alpha$ of B$^+$ and A$^-$ ions, thus

$$BA \quad \rightleftharpoons B^+ + A^-$$
$$C(1 - \alpha) \quad C\alpha \quad C\alpha$$

The equilibrium constant for the dissociation process is given by

$$K' \approx \frac{[B^+][A^-]}{[BA]} = \frac{\alpha^2 C}{(1 - \alpha)} \tag{3.1}$$

The approximation sign is due to the fact that concentrations have been used in place of activities and K' refers to the *apparent* equilibrium constant.

Equation (3.1) has become known as the Ostwald dilution law and, for a very weak electrolyte where $\alpha \ll 1$, takes the form $K' \approx \alpha^2 C$. For weak electrolytes, K' shows fair constancy over a range of low concentrations.

3.2   The Brønsted–Lowry concept of acids and bases

In studies of catalysis of solution reactions by acids and bases, Brønsted observed that catalytic activity was shown by species which at the time were not regarded as acids or bases. An extension of the classical view of acids and bases became desirable and a general definition of such substances to include both aqueous and non-aqueous media was necessary.

Earlier definitions of acids and bases as species producing respectively hydrogen ions and hydroxyl ions are only valid in aqueous solution. The concept of Brønsted and Lowry, while *extending* the classical definition, does not exclude the treatment of Arrhenius for aqueous media. The extended view regards acids as proton donors and bases as proton acceptors regardless of whether substances concerned are ionic or neutral. A terse summary of this definition may be given as follows

$$acid \rightleftharpoons base + proton \tag{3.2}$$

As examples, the following equilibria may be cited

$$H_2SO_4 \rightleftharpoons HSO_4^- + H^+$$
$$HSO_4^- \rightleftharpoons SO_4^{2-} + H^+$$

$$H_3O^+ \rightleftharpoons H_2O + H^+$$

$$H_2O \rightleftharpoons OH^- + H^+$$

$$OH^- \rightleftharpoons O^{2-} + H^+ \tag{3.3}$$

The species on the right-hand side of Equation (3.3), along with the protons, are in each case what are known as the *conjugate bases* of the various acids. In a similar way one may define conjugate acids of appropriate bases. It is apparent that some species, known as ampholytes, are capable of behaving as both acids and bases. In this respect the nature of water when acting as a solvent is of particular significance, as it means that all acidic and basic properties in aqueous solution will set up equilibria involving the solvent.

Owing to the fact that unsolvated protons cannot exist in solution, Equations (3.3) are meaningless as written. They may, however, prove useful when considering coupled acid–base systems provided that it is borne in mind that H^+ refers to the *solvated* proton. Thus, the reaction of sulphuric acid and ammonia may be considered as

$$H_2SO_4 \rightleftharpoons HSO_4^- + H^+$$

$$\underline{NH_3 + H^+ \rightleftharpoons NH_4^+}$$

$$H_2SO_4 + NH_3 \rightleftharpoons HSO_4^- + NH_4^+ \tag{3.4}$$

Or, in general,

$$acid_1 + base_2 \rightleftharpoons base_1 + acid_2 \tag{3.5}$$

where $base_1$ is the conjugate base of the original $acid_1$ and $acid_2$ is the conjugate acid of the original $base_2$.

The position of equilibrium in such systems is determined by the relative *strengths* of the two acids and bases. If $acid_1$ is stronger than $acid_2$ or, which comes to the same thing, if $base_2$ is stronger than $base_1$, the equilibrium is displaced to the right. To such reversible systems the Law of Mass Action applies, so that we may write for the equilibrium constant

$$K \sim \frac{[base_1][acid_2]}{[acid_1][base_2]} \tag{3.6}$$

where K is dependent only upon temperature and the nature of the solvent. The approximation sign takes account of the fact that concentrations have been used in place of activities. Equation (3.6) may be used for dilute solutions where the effects of ion interaction are minimized.

3.3   Strengths of acids and bases in aqueous solution

We have referred somewhat vaguely above to the relative strengths of acids and bases. It is now necessary to give quantitative significance to such terms. The strengths of acids for a particular solvent are measured and expressed with respect to a chosen standard *for that solvent.* Thus, for water, the standard is the acid–base pair H_3O^+/H_2O. The strength of some other acid, A, may then be defined with respect to the reaction

$$A + H_2O \rightleftharpoons B + H_3O^+$$

e.g.

$$CH_3COOH + H_2O \rightleftharpoons CH_3COO^- + H_3O^+ \tag{3.7}$$

B being the conjugate *base* of the *acid* A. The equilibrium constant for this reaction is then a measure of the strength of A in that it defines the extent to which the reaction proceeds to the left or right, i.e.,

$$K = \frac{[B][H_3O^+]}{[A][H_2O]}$$

or

$$K_a = \frac{[B][H_3O^+]}{[A]} \tag{3.8}$$

where $K_a = K[H_2O]$, the term $[H_2O]$ being omitted from the denominator and absorbed into the constant K_a, since it is very large and approximately constant for dilute solution. If the acid A is the water molecule, the equilibrium constant refers to the self-ionization of water, viz

$$H_2O + H_2O \rightleftharpoons H_3O^+ + OH^-$$

for which

$$K = \frac{[H_3O^+][OH^-]}{[H_2O]^2} \tag{3.9}$$

It is usual to express the equilibrium constant for this case as

$$K_W = [H_3O^+][OH^-] \tag{3.10}$$

29

where K_W is known as the *ionic product* of water which has approximately the value 1×10^{-14} at 298 K. We saw that reaction (3.5) lay to the right when $base_2$ was stronger than $base_1$ and $acid_1$ stronger than $acid_2$. This infers the general finding that a strong acid or base tends to produce a weak conjugate base or acid. In fact, some workers represent the strength of a base as the inverse of the dissociation constant of the corresponding conjugate acid. In this way it is possible to use a single dissociation constant to define the properties of an acid–base pair A/B, viz.

$$K = \frac{[B][H_3O^+]}{[A]} \tag{3.11}$$

Then the greater the strength of A and the smaller that of B, the higher is the value of K and the smaller the value of $1/K$.

Since the above treatment is not generally adopted, we shall also consider the more conventional definition of base strength in terms of the hydroxyl ions produced in water, e.g., for the reaction

$$NH_3 + H_2O \rightleftharpoons NH_4^+ + OH^- \tag{3.12}$$

(with water now behaving as an acid) we may write the dissociation constant, K_b, of the base as

$$K_b = \frac{[NH_4^+][OH^-]}{[NH_3]} \tag{3.13}$$

where, again, $[H_2O]$ being approximately constant, is absorbed into K_b. Equation (3.13) may be developed by multiplying numerator and denominator of the right-hand side by K_W, thus

$$K_b = \frac{[NH_4^+][OH^-]}{[NH_3]} \frac{K_W}{[H_3O^+][OH^-]} \tag{3.14}$$

therefore

$$K_b = \frac{[NH_4^+]}{[NH_3][H_3O^+]} K_W \tag{3.15}$$

Now,

$$\frac{[NH_4^+]}{[NH_3][H_3O^+]} = \frac{1}{K_a} \tag{3.16}$$

30

where K_a is the acid dissociation constant of the conjugate acid of NH_3, the ammonium cation, referring to the reaction

$$NH_4^+ + H_2O \rightleftharpoons NH_3 + H_3O^+ \qquad (3.17)$$

Thus,

$$K_b = \frac{K_W}{K_a} \qquad \text{or} \qquad K_a = \frac{K_W}{K_b} \qquad (3.18)$$

The dissociation constant of an acid or base may therefore be given by K_W divided by the dissociation constant of the corresponding conjugate base or acid.

Experimental values of K_a, K_b vary over many orders of magnitude. Rather than deal with such an unwieldy range of values, it is more convenient to express strengths of acids or bases on a logarithmic scale. The logarithmic exponent (pK) of a dissociation constant is defined as

$$pK = -\log_{10} K \qquad (3.19)$$

the negative sign indicating that a high pK value is to imply a weaker acid and stronger base while a low value implies a stronger acid and weaker base.

3.4   Hydrolysis

Reactions such as

$$CH_3COO^- + H_2O \rightleftharpoons CH_3COOH + OH^- \qquad (3.20)$$

and

$$NH_4^+ + H_2O \rightleftharpoons NH_3 + H_3O^+ \qquad (3.21)$$

are hydrolysis reactions for salts of a weak acid and base respectively. In the first case it is also necessary to have cations and in the second anions present in solution, since an individual ion species cannot exist on its own. If these other ions do not show acidic or basic character they may be considered as playing no part in the hydrolysis equilibria.

The equilibrium constant, known as the hydrolysis or hydrolytic constant,

K_h, for reaction (3.20) is given by

$$K_h = \frac{[CH_3COOH][OH^-]}{[CH_3COO^-]} = K_b = \frac{K_W}{K_a} \qquad (3.22)$$

It is seen that K_h is identical to the *base* dissociation constant of the *acetate* ion and may therefore be related through K_W to the *acid* dissociation constant of the parent acid.

For hydrolysis (3.21) we may now write

$$K_h = \frac{[NH_3][H_3O^+]}{[NH_4^+]} = K_a = \frac{K_W}{K_b} \qquad (3.23)$$

where K_h identifies with the *acid* dissociation constant of the ammonium ion and may be related via K_W to the base dissociation constant of the parent base.

Further, Equations (3.20) and (3.21) show that the solution of the salt of a weak acid and a strong base has an alkaline reaction while that of the salt of a weak base and a strong acid has an acid reaction.

In water, a salt derived from both a weak acid and a weak base will show participation in such reactions by both cation and anion. As an example, the case of ammonium acetate may be considered

$$NH_4^+ + H_2O \rightleftharpoons NH_3 + H_3O^+; \qquad K_a' = \frac{[NH_3][H_3O^+]}{[NH_4^+]}$$

$$CH_3COO^- + H_2O \rightleftharpoons CH_3COOH + OH^-; \qquad K_b' = \frac{[CH_3COOH][OH^-]}{[CH_3COO^-]}$$

Overall

$$NH_4^+ + CH_3COO^- + 2H_2O \rightleftharpoons NH_3 + CH_3COOH + H_3O^+ + OH^- \qquad (3.24)$$

for which the equilibrium constant, K, is given by

$$K = \frac{[NH_3][CH_3COOH][H_3O^+][OH^-]}{[NH_4^+][CH_3COO^-]} = K_a' K_b' \qquad (3.25)$$

i.e.

$$\frac{K'_a K'_b}{K_W} = \frac{[CH_3COOH][NH_3]}{[NH_4^+][CH_3COO^-]} = \text{constant} = K_h \qquad (3.26)$$

Now K'_a is the dissociation constant of the acid NH_4^+ which is related to the dissociation constant, K_b, of the base NH_3 by

$$K'_a = \frac{K_W}{K_b}$$

Also, K'_b is the dissociation constant of the base CH_3COO^- which is related to the dissociation constant, K_a, of the acid CH_3COOH by

$$K'_b = \frac{K_W}{K_a}$$

Therefore,

$$K_h = \frac{K_W \cdot K_W}{K_W \cdot K_a \cdot K_b} = \frac{K_W}{K_a K_b} \qquad (3.27)$$

3.5 The extent of acidity. The pH scale

A consideration of the self-ionization of water,

$$2 H_2O \rightleftharpoons H_3O^+ + OH^-$$

makes it clear that this solvent is neutral owing to equal concentrations of H_3O^+ and OH^- ions. At 298 K each of these is equal to 10^{-7} mol dm^{-3}. It must be remembered that, since K_W is temperature dependent, so also is the concentration of H_3O^+ and OH^- corresponding to the condition of neutrality.

Owing to the vast range of acidity possible, concentrations of H_3O^+ and OH^- are better expressed in logarithmic form in the same way as dissociation constants. Again, negative exponents are considered, thus,

$$pH = -\log a_{H_3O^+} \sim -\log[H_3O^+] \qquad (3.28)$$

and

$$pOH = -\log[OH^-]$$

33

also

$$\log[H_3O^+] + \log[OH^-] = \log K_W \qquad (3.29)$$

or,

$$pH + pOH = pK_W = 14 \text{ at } 298 \text{ K} \qquad (3.30)$$

so that for most practical purposes the scale may be regarded as extending from 0 to 14.

These simple relationships may be used to calculate the pH of solutions of each type of salt considered in section 3.4.

3.5.1 Salts derived from weak acids and strong bases

If we take as our example the case of sodium acetate, the hydrolysis reaction is that represented by Equation (3.20) for which we wrote

$$K_h = \frac{[CH_3COOH][OH^-]}{[CH_3COO^-]} \qquad \text{(see Equation (3.22))}$$

Since $[CH_3COOH] = [OH^-]$, we may write

$$K_h = \frac{[OH^-]^2}{[CH_3COO^-]} \qquad (3.31)$$

If the degree of hydrolysis is small, which in practical terms means a K_h value less than 0·01, $[CH_3COO^-]$ is approximately the concentration of sodium acetate, C, originally dissolved. Thus,

$$K_h \sim \frac{[OH^-]^2}{C}$$

and

$$[OH^-] \sim \sqrt{(K_h C)} \qquad (3.32)$$

therefore,

$$[H_3O^+] = \frac{K_W}{[OH^-]} \sim \frac{K_W}{\sqrt{(K_h C)}}$$

and

$$[H_3O^+] = \left(\frac{K_W K_a}{C}\right)^{1/2}$$

Or, taking logarithms

$$pH = \tfrac{1}{2}(pK_W + pK_a + \log C) \tag{3.33}$$

3.5.2 Salts derived from weak bases and strong acids

An example of such a salt is ammonium chloride whose hydrolysis reaction is that represented by Equation (3.21) from which the hydrolysis constant is given by

$$K_h = \frac{[NH_3][H_3O^+]}{[NH_4^+]} \qquad \text{(see Equation (3.23))}$$

Since $[NH_3] = [H_3O^+]$, we may write

$$K_h = \frac{[H_3O^+]^2}{[NH_4^+]} \tag{3.34}$$

Also, if K_h is small, $[NH_4^+] \sim C$, the concentration of ammonium chloride taken, so that

$$[H_3O^+] \sim \sqrt{(K_h C)}$$
$$= \left(\frac{K_W C}{K_b}\right)^{1/2}$$

or, taking logarithms,

$$pH = \tfrac{1}{2}(pK_W - pK_b - \log C) \tag{3.35}$$

3.5.3 Salts derived from weak bases and weak acids

In the case of ammonium acetate we have, from Equation (3.27),

$$K_h = \frac{K_W}{K_a K_b}$$

Let us suppose that the original concentration of dissolved salt is C and that $[NH_3] \sim [CH_3COOH]$ i.e. the two hydrolysis reactions have proceeded to the same extent. Also, if K_h is small $[NH_4^+]$ and $[CH_3COO^-]$ are both approximately C. K_h is given, by Equation (3.26) and in terms of the above approximations, by

$$K_h = \frac{[NH_3][CH_3COOH]}{[NH_4^+][CH_3COO^-]} \sim \frac{[CH_3COOH]^2}{C^2}$$

or,

$$[CH_3COOH] = CK_h^{1/2} = C\left(\frac{K_W}{K_a K_b}\right)^{1/2} \tag{3.36}$$

Now K_a for the parent acid is given by

$$K_a = \frac{[CH_3COO^-][H_3O^+]}{[CH_3COOH]}$$

so that,

$$[CH_3COOH] = \frac{C[H_3O^+]}{K_a} \tag{3.37}$$

from Equations (3.36) and (3.37) we obtain

$$[H_3O^+] = \left(\frac{K_a K_W}{K_b}\right)^{1/2}$$

or, taking logarithms,

$$pH = \tfrac{1}{2}(pK_W + pK_a - pK_b) \tag{3.38}$$

3.6   Buffer systems

Buffer systems consist of weak acids or bases dissolved in company with one of their completely ionized salts. The purpose of such systems is to maintain an almost constant pH which is only slightly affected by the addition of acids or bases.

Consider the system acetic acid/sodium acetate in which the state of ionization of the various species may be represented as follows:

$$CH_3COOH + H_2O \rightleftharpoons CH_3COO^- + H_3O^+$$
$$CH_3COO^- + Na^+$$

The presence of the fully dissociated acetate salt will suppress the protolysis of the acid so that this remains virtually undissociated. This means that the concentration of free acetic acid, $[CH_3COOH]$, in the system is to all intents and purposes the original concentration, $[acid]_0$. Similarly, the concentration of acetate ion $[CH_3COO^-]$ is very close to that of the salt, $[salt]_0$.

Thus the acid dissociation constant may be given in the form

$$K_a \sim \frac{[salt]_0}{[acid]_0} \cdot [H_3O^+]$$

or

$$[H_3O^+] \sim K_a \frac{[acid]_0}{[salt]_0} \qquad (3.39)$$

or, taking logarithms,

$$pH = pK_a + \log \frac{[salt]_0}{[acid]_0} \qquad (3.40)$$

Equation (3.40) is one form of the Henderson–Hasselbalch equation which states that the pH of a buffer solution is a function of the dissociation constant of the weak acid and the acid/salt ratio. In some circumstances this latter quantity may simply be calculated from the known quantities of the two components used to make up the buffer solution.

For a weak base in company with one of its completely ionized salts the argument is similar. Consider the case of ammonia in the presence of ammonium chloride.

$$NH_3 + H_2O \rightleftharpoons NH_4^+ + OH^-$$
$$NH_4^+ + Cl^-$$

Since the ammonium chloride is almost completely dissociated, $[NH_4^+] \sim [salt]_0$ and $[NH_3] \sim [base]_0$, so that we may write for K_b,

$$K_b = \frac{[salt]_0}{[base]_0} [OH^-] \qquad (3.41)$$

therefore,

$$[OH^-] = \frac{[base]_0}{[salt]_0} \cdot K_b$$

or,

$$pH = pK_W - pK_b - \log \frac{[\text{salt}]_0}{[\text{base}]_0} \qquad (3.42)$$

This is a further form of the Henderson–Hasselbalch equation being equivalent to Equation (3.40). Addition of small amounts of strong acids and bases serve only to interconvert small amounts of the weak acid or base and the salt comprising the buffer so that the concentration ratio remains almost constant. The most effective buffers have this ratio of the order of unity.

The efficiency of a buffer system is measured in terms of its 'buffer capacity', β, which, for an acidic buffer may be defined by

$$\beta = \frac{d[B]}{dpH} \qquad (3.43)$$

Equation (3.43) gives β as the change of concentration of strong base, $d[B]$, which is required for a given pH change. For a basic buffer, the buffer capacity is given by

$$\beta = -\frac{d[A]}{dpH} \qquad (3.44)$$

where $d[A]$ is now the change of concentration of strong acid required to produce the change dpH.

Acidic buffer solutions may be prepared by mixing a weak acid, HA and a strong base, BOH, so that the following interaction occurs

$$HA + BOH \rightleftharpoons B^+ + A^- + H_3O^+$$

the pH of the resulting solution being given by

$$pH = pK_a + \log \frac{[A^-]}{[HA]}$$

$$= pK_a + \log \frac{x}{a-x} \qquad (3.45)$$

where $a = [HA] + [A^-]$ and $x = [B^+]$.

β is obtained from this expression by differentiation as

$$\beta = \frac{d[B]}{dpH} = \frac{dx}{dpH} = 2 \cdot 303 x \left(1 - \frac{x}{a}\right) \qquad (3.46)$$

Basic buffer solutions may be prepared by mixing a weak base and strong acid so that the following interaction occurs

$$BOH + HA \rightleftharpoons BH^+ + A^- + OH^-$$

the pH of the resulting solution now being given by

$$pH = pK_W - pK_b + \log \frac{[BOH]}{[BH^+]}$$

$$= pK_W - pK_b + \log \frac{a - x}{x} \tag{3.47}$$

where $a = [BOH] + [BH^+]$ and $x = [BH^+]$. Here β becomes

$$\beta = -\frac{dx}{dpH} = 2 \cdot 303x\left(\frac{x}{a} - 1\right) \tag{3.48}$$

Buffering is only satisfactory when the salt/acid or salt/base ratios lie between 0·1 and 10 so that the *effective* buffer range of any system, in terms of the dissociation constants of the acid or base involved, is given by

$$pH = pK_a \pm 1$$

and

$$pOH = pK_b \pm 1 \tag{3.49}$$

The variation of buffer capacity with variation of the salt/acid ratio is shown in Fig. 3.1.

It is seen from Equations (3.46) and (3.48) that for β to be a maximum, $d\beta/dx = 0$, i.e. $x_{max} = \frac{1}{2}a$, which corresponds to a 1 : 1 ratio of acid or base to salt. It is clear from Equation (3.45) that, under the above conditions, $pH = pK_a$. The variation of β with pH is shown in Fig. 3.2.

Calculations of pH from the given forms of the Henderson–Hasselbalch equation are only valid when the buffer ratios may be calculated from the quantities of components used to make the solution. Such procedure is only justified for the range $4 < pH < 10$; outside this range, the values of concentrations involved in the buffer ratio will differ considerably from those initially dissolved. Consider firstly the case of a solution with $pH < 4$ containing a buffer system represented by HA/A^-. It is now no longer true to say that very little acid will ionize; it is of sufficient strength that the amount of

39

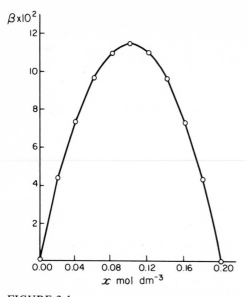

FIGURE 3.1
Variation of buffer capacity for an acid buffer with the proportion of salt to acid. Points calculated from Equation (3.46) using $a = 0.2$ mol dm^{-3}; $x = 0$–0.2 mol dm^{-3}.

free unionized acid is significantly less than that originally dissolved. There is correspondingly more of the anion, A^-, than can be accounted for by the total ionization of the salt alone. In order to establish the amounts of free acid and anion that will be present in the buffer system, it is necessary to consider the equilibrium

$$HA + H_2O \rightleftharpoons H_3O^+ + A^-$$

from which it is readily seen that

$$[HA] = [HA]_0 - [H_3O^+]$$

and

$$[A^-] = [A^-]_0 + [H_3O^+]$$

The Henderson–Hasselbalch equation now takes the form

$$pH = pK_a + \log \frac{[A^-]_0 + [H_3O^+]}{[HA]_0 - [H_3O^+]} \qquad (3.50)$$

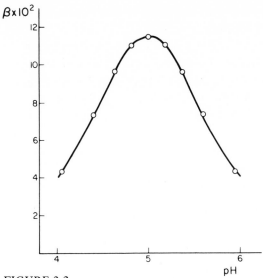

FIGURE 3.2
Variation of buffer capacity with pH for an acid buffer. Points calculated from Equations (3.46) and (3.45) using $pK_a = 5$; $a = 0\cdot2$ mol dm^{-3}

Similar arguments hold for a buffer system of pH greater than 10, which we may represent by B/BH$^+$. It is now necessary to make suitable allowance for the equilibrium

$$B + H_2O \rightleftharpoons BH^+ + OH^-$$

The base now ionizes to a far from neglible extent so that $[B] < [B]_0$ and $[B] = [B]_0 - [OH^-]$. Further, $[BH^+]_0$ is now supplemented by further BH$^+$ produced by the above reaction, so that $[BH^+] = [BH^+]_0 + [OH^-]$. Thus,

$$pH = pK_W - pK_b - \log \frac{[BH^+]_0 + [OH^-]}{[B]_0 - [OH^-]} \qquad (3.51)$$

3.7   Acid-base indicators

In an acid–base titration there will only be observed a pH of 7 at the equivalence point if *both* titrant and titrand are strong electrolytes. If one is weak,

41

the salt formed will undergo hydrolysis and the solution at the equivalence point will be either slightly acid or alkaline.

Acid–base indicators show differing colours with varying hydrogen ion concentration in a solution. The change in colour occurs in general over a 'colour change interval' of some two pH units. It is necessary to select indicators for particular titrations which show clear colours at pH values close to those known to hold at the equivalence point.

Indicators are themselves weak organic acids or bases whose undissociated forms differ in colour from the ionic forms due to their considerably different electronic structure and hence absorption spectra.

The dissociation of an acid indicator molecule in water occurs according to

$$\underset{\text{colour 1}}{HIn} + H_2O \rightleftharpoons H_3O^+ + \underset{\text{colour 2}}{In^-} \qquad (3.52)$$

In dilute solution the equilibrium constant, K_i, for this reaction is

$$K_i = \frac{[H_3O^+][In^-]}{[HIn]} \qquad (3.53)$$

from which

$$[H_3O^+] = K_i \frac{[HIn]}{[In^-]} \qquad (3.54)$$

or,

$$pH = pK_i + \log \frac{[In^-]}{[HIn]} \qquad (3.55)$$

The *titration exponent*, pK_i, may be defined as the pH at which the concentrations of basic (In^-) and acidic (HIn) forms of the indicator are equal.

Phenolphthalein is an acid indicator of this type with acidic and basic species given in Fig. 3.3. Alternatively, Equation (3.54) may be expressed in terms of the fraction, x, of indicator in the alkaline form

$$[H_3O^+] = K_i \frac{1-x}{x} \qquad (3.56)$$

This latter is sometimes known as the *indicator equation*.

More correctly, Equation (3.55) should have the term $\log \gamma_{In^-}/\gamma_{HIn}$ added

colourless acid   red anion

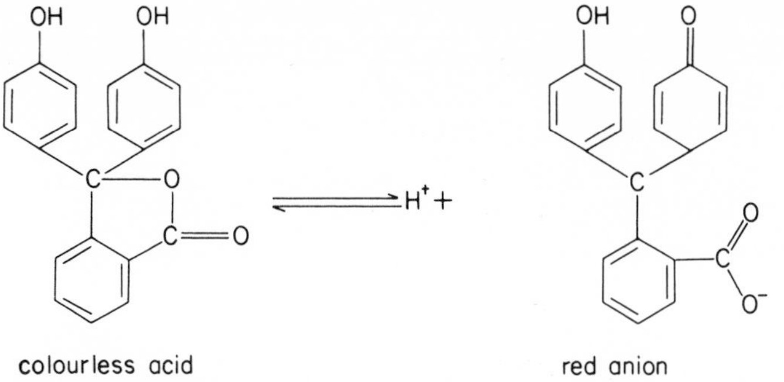

FIGURE 3.3
The acidic and anionic forms of phenolphthalein.

to its right-hand side. However, since the solution is dilute and HIn is non-ionic, $\gamma_{HIn} \sim 1$, so that Equation (3.55), with account taken of significant activity coefficients, becomes

$$pH = pK_i + \log \frac{[In^-]}{[HIn]} + \log \gamma_{In^-} \qquad (3.57)$$

This, in terms of the Debye–Hückel expression for the anion activity coefficient, becomes

$$pH = pK_i + \log \frac{[In^-]}{[HIn]} - 0.5z^2 I^{\frac{1}{2}} \qquad (3.58)$$

z being the charge on the anion and I the ionic strength of the solution. For many practical purposes the last term of Equation (3.58) may be omitted, Equation (3.55) being sufficiently accurate.

Equation (3.56) is quite general, applying to both indicator acids and indicator bases.

It is found in practice that an observer can normally detect no change from a full acid or full alkaline colour until at least 9% of the indicator is in the alkaline- or acid-coloured form respectively. Thus in passing from an acid to an alkaline solution, no change in colour is apparent until 9% of the indicator assumes the alkaline form, i.e. $x = 0.09$ and $1 - x = 0.91$. Insertion of these values into Equation (3.56) gives

$$[H_3O^+] = \frac{0.91}{0.09} K_i \sim 10K_i$$

43

or

$$pH = pK_i - 1 \qquad (3.59)$$

Similarly, in passing from alkaline to acid solution,

$$[H_3O^+] = \frac{0\cdot09}{0\cdot91} K_i \sim 0\cdot1K_i$$

or

$$pH = pK_i + 1 \qquad (3.60)$$

The effective range of pH over which colour changes can be detected is therefore given by

$$pH = pK_i \pm 1 \qquad (3.61)$$

3.8 General acid–base theory and non-aqueous solvents

The general relationship,

$$acid_1 + base_2 \rightleftharpoons base_1 + acid_2 \qquad \text{(see Equation (3.5))}$$

may be applied quite generally to all dissociation processes, e.g. to acid dissociations such as

$$HNO_3 + H_2O \rightleftharpoons NO_3^- + H_3O^+ \qquad (3.62)$$

and to self-ionization (or autoprotolytic) reactions such as

$$H_2O + H_2O \rightleftharpoons H_3O^+ + OH^-$$
$$NH_3 + NH_3 \rightleftharpoons NH_4^+ + NH_2^-$$
$$C_2H_5OH + C_2H_5OH \rightleftharpoons C_2H_5O^- + C_2H_5OH_2^+$$
$$H_2SO_4 + H_2SO_4 \rightleftharpoons HSO_4^- + H_3SO_4^+ \qquad (3.63)$$

The latter processes are important for almost all solvents.

There are four types of solvent which may be distinguished in terms of acid–base theory:

(1) *Acidic* or protogenic solvents. These provide protons, common examples being sulphuric and acetic acids.

44

(2) *Basic* or protophilic solvents. These have the ability to bind protons, liquid ammonia being typical.

(3) *Amphoteric* or amphiprotic solvents such as water and ethanol which behave as either acids or bases.

(4) *Aprotic* solvents. Such solvents show no self-ionization. Most, like benzene, do not take part in protolytic reactions although some, such as dimethylformamide and dimethylsulphoxide show basic properties.

In autoprotic reactions the term *lyonium* ion is often given to the ion species resulting from proton solvation (e.g. H_3O^+, NH_4^+) while the solvent residue (less the proton) is called the *lyate* ion (e.g. $C_2H_5O^-$, NH_2^-).

The proton affinities of the solvent and its lyate ion decide the acid–base characteristics of a particular solute in that solvent. Thus, if a solute has a greater proton affinity than that of the lyate ion deriving from the solvent, it will behave as a base in that solvent. On the other hand, if the conjugate base to a solute has a smaller proton affinity than the solvent itself, the solute behaves as an acid.

Thus, the conjugate base of benzoic acid, $C_6H_5COO^-$, has less affinity for protons than water so that the reaction

$$C_6H_5COOH + H_2O \rightleftharpoons C_6H_5COO^- + H_3O^+ \qquad (3.64)$$

occurs in aqueous solution which is in accord with experience, benzoic acid behaving as a weak acid in aqueous solution. This, however, is not the case in concentrated sulphuric acid. Here benzoic acid has a greater proton affinity than the lyate ion from sulphuric acid, HSO_4^-, so that the reaction

$$C_6H_5COOH + H_2SO_4 \rightleftharpoons C_6H_5COOH_2^+ + HSO_4^- \qquad (3.65)$$

occurs in this medium, i.e. benzoic acid is now behaving as a base.

Aniline in liquid ammonia behaves as a weak acid because the solvent has a rather greater affinity for protons than does the species $C_6H_5NH^-$

$$C_6H_5NH_2 + NH_3 \rightleftharpoons C_6H_5NH^- + NH_4^+ \qquad (3.66)$$

On the other hand, in glacial acetic acid, aniline has a much greater proton affinity than does the lyate ion CH_3COO^- and so behaves as a strong base

$$C_6H_5NH_2 + CH_3COOH \rightleftharpoons C_6H_5NH_3^+ + CH_3COO^- \qquad (3.67)$$

45

The Brønsted theory defines the strengths of acids and bases in terms of acidity and basicity constants defined by

$$K_{a,A} = \frac{a_{H^+}a_B}{a_A}; \qquad K_{b,B} = \frac{a_A}{a_{H^+}a_B} \qquad (3.68)$$

where $K_{a,A}$, $K_{b,B}$ are *thermodynamic* acidity and basicity constants respectively. Note that $K_{a,A} \cdot K_{b,B} = 1$ for a conjugate acid-base pair.

Further constants, known as *rational* acidity and basicity constants have been introduced to avoid use of the unattainable activities of A and B. These are defined by

$$K_{A,A} = \frac{a_{H^+}[B]}{[A]}; \qquad K_{B,B} = \frac{[A]}{a_{H^+}[B]} \qquad (3.69)$$

for which again $K_{A,A} \cdot K_{B,B} = 1$.

Now let us apply this concept of rational constants to an amphiprotic solvent, S; a number of possibilities arise

(1) $$S \rightleftharpoons S^- + H^+ \qquad (3.70)$$

i.e. the solvent acts as an acid for which the rational acidity constant, $K_{A,S}$ is given by

$$K_{A,S} = \frac{a_{H^+}[S^-]}{[S]} \qquad \text{or} \qquad K'_{A,S} = a_{H^+}[S^-] \qquad (3.71)$$

(2) $$S^- + H^+ \rightleftharpoons S \qquad (3.72)$$

Here the conjugate base or lyate ion, S^-, takes up a proton; the rational basicity constant of this ion is given by

$$K_{B,S^-} = \frac{[S]}{a_{H^+}[S^-]} \qquad \text{or} \qquad K'_{B,S^-} = \frac{1}{a_{H^+}[S^-]} \qquad (3.73)$$

(3) $$S^+ \rightleftharpoons S + H^+ \qquad (3.74)$$

i.e. the acid or lyonium ion gives up a proton, so that

$$K_{A,S^+} = \frac{a_{H^+}[S]}{[S^+]} \qquad \text{or} \qquad K'_{A,S^+} = \frac{a_{H^+}}{[S^+]} \qquad (3.75)$$

(4) $$S + H^+ \rightleftharpoons S^+$$

Here the solvent acts as a base for which

$$K_{B,S} = \frac{[S^+]}{a_{H^+}[S]} \quad \text{or} \quad K'_{B,S} = \frac{[S^+]}{a_{H^+}} \tag{3.76}$$

The constants denoted K' are known as *conventional* acidity and basicity constants. In these, S is absorbed into the rational constant – a procedure justified on account of the small extent of ionization of amphiprotic solvents.

In an exactly analogous manner three types of protolysis constant may be introduced for reactions such as $A_1 + B_2 \rightleftharpoons B_1 + A_2$. Thus

$$K_{a_1,b_2} = \frac{a_{B_1} a_{A_2}}{a_{A_1} a_{B_2}} \quad \text{the } \textit{thermodynamic} \text{ protolytic constant} \tag{3.77}$$

and

$$K_{A_1,B_2} = \frac{[B_1][A_2]}{[A_1][B_2]} \quad \text{the } \textit{rational} \text{ protolytic constant} \tag{3.78}$$

These latter constants, unlike acidity and basicity constants are measurable. Acidity and basicity constants are defined with reference to reactions which do not occur in isolation.

If one of the reactants is the solvent (3.78) takes the forms

$$K'_{A,S} = \frac{[B][S^+]}{[A]} \tag{3.79a}$$

for $A + S \rightleftharpoons B + S^+$ and

$$K'_{B,S} = \frac{[A][S^-]}{[B]} \tag{3.79b}$$

for $B + S \rightleftharpoons A + S^-$.

Further, for the autoprotolysis reaction between two solvent molecules, thermodynamic, rational and conventional autoprotolysis constants are definable. Such reactions may in general be expressed by

$$S + S \rightleftharpoons S^+ + S^-$$

for which

$$K_{s,s} = \frac{a_{S^+} a_{S^-}}{a_S^2} \qquad \text{(thermodynamic)} \qquad (3.80a)$$

$$K_{S,S} = \frac{[S^+][S^-]}{[S]^2} \qquad \text{(rational)} \qquad (3.80b)$$

and

$$K'_{S,S} = [S^+][S^-] \qquad \text{(conventional)} \qquad (3.80c)$$

The fact that acidity and basicity constants are not experimentally determinable means that the acidity of a solution cannot be expressed practically in terms of such constants. The quantities which *are* determinable are the protolysis constants, the thermodynamic values of which are obtained from directly determined rational constants over a range of ionic strengths and extrapolation to zero ionic strength. Protolysis constants, however, refer to reactions of the type $A_1 + B_2 \rightleftharpoons B_1 + A_2$ involving conjugate acid–base pairs so that they only represent the *relative* strengths of the acids A_1 and A_2 involved. In order to be able to compare the strengths of a whole range of acids it is necessary to choose one acid as a standard which we may symbolize A_0. A protolytic reaction involving this acid may then be represented by

$$A + B_0 \rightleftharpoons B + A_0$$

and may be regarded as made up of the two separate acid reactions (with solvent ignored)

$$A \rightleftharpoons B + H^+$$

and

$$A_0 \rightleftharpoons B_0 + H^+$$

The ratio of rational acidity constants is given by

$$\frac{K_{A,A}}{K_{A,A_0}} = \frac{[B][H^+]}{[A]} \Big/ \frac{[B_0][H^+]}{[A_0]}$$

$$= K_{A,A} \cdot K_{B,B_0}, \qquad (3.81)$$

which we may now express as $K_{A,A}^{A,0}$, the relative acidity constant.

The reference acid may be either the lyonium ion corresponding to the solvent (i.e. its conjugate acid) or an indicator. It is the H_3O^+ ion which is responsible for the acidity of aqueous solutions which may be expressed on the pH scale defined by

$$pH = -\log a_{H_3O^+} = -\log m_{H_3O^+}\gamma_{H_3O^+} \qquad (3.82)$$

This formal definition, however, cannot be employed directly in practice due to the impossibility of determining $a_{H_3O^+}$. Instead, a *conventional* scale has to be used which approaches the formal one (this will be considered later). The pH scale is, of course, only applicable to aqueous solutions. Although an acidity scale may be drawn up for a given solvent in terms of the concentration of the appropriate lyonium ion, SH^+, it will be specific for that medium. By this means as many scales of acidity as there are solvents available may be drawn up but with the disadvantage that comparison of values on one scale with those on another is meaningless.

The only solute species common to all solvents is the proton, and it is with respect to this species that any universal scale must be drawn up. The solvation of protons will occur to different extents in different solvents

$$S + H^+ \rightleftharpoons SH^+$$

and may be expressed by the equilibrium constant $K_{solv} = a_{H^+}/a_{SH^+}$.

While such equilibrium constants cannot be determined experimentally, the ratio for two different solvents is accessible. For reaction of a given acid in two solvents S_1 and S_2 we have the equilibria

$$A + S_1 \rightleftharpoons B + S_1H^+$$

and

$$A + S_2 \rightleftharpoons B + S_2H^+$$

with rational protolysis constants

$$K_{AS_1} = \frac{[B]_1[S_1H^+]}{[A]_1[S_1]} \quad \text{and} \quad K_{AS_2} = \frac{[B]_2[S_2H^+]}{[A]_2[S_2]}$$

respectively, from which $(K_{solv})_1/(K_{solv})_2$ may be found. If water is used as reference solvent, with K_{solv} for this case given the value unity, the scale coincides with the pH scale for aqueous solutions.

49

Hammett defined what he termed the acidity function, H_0, in terms of the behaviour of a series of colour indicators, B. For a given indicator H_0 is defined by reference to the reaction

$$B + H^+ \rightleftharpoons BH^+$$

where

$$K = \frac{[BH^+]}{[B][H^+]} \cdot \frac{\gamma_{BH^+}}{\gamma_B \gamma_{H^+}}$$

or

$$\log K - \log \frac{[BH^+]}{[B]} = -\log a_{H^+} - \log \frac{\gamma_B}{\gamma_{BH^+}} \qquad (3.83)$$

or

$$(pK_a)_{BH^+} + \log \frac{[B]}{[BH^+]} = -\log a_{H^+} - \log \frac{\gamma_B}{\gamma_{BH^+}} = H_0 \qquad (3.84)$$

By analogy with the corresponding equation for pH, it is seen that when $[B]/[BH^+] = 1$, $H_0 = (pK_a)_{BH^+}$. We have already seen that a given indicator is only of use in the range $0.1 < [B]/[BH^+] < 10$, so that for one indicator values of H_0 can only cover at best the range

$$H_0 = (pK_a)_{BH^+} \pm 1 \qquad (3.85)$$

A series of indicators must be used to cover a wide range of H_0 values.

If the species BH^+ and B are distinguishable spectrophotometrically, the ratio of their concentrations may be measured and H_0 determined by Equation (3.84). If, further, it is assumed that for a series of indicators of the same charge type (such as the anilines) $\gamma_B/\gamma_{BH^+} \sim$ constant, H_0 may be determined for any acidic solution if a suitable indicator is used by measuring $[B]/[BH^+]$ and $(pK_a)_{BH^+}$.

It is seen from Equation (3.84) that in dilute aqueous solution the H_0 scale coincides with the pH scale, since then $\gamma_B/\gamma_{BH^+} \sim 1$.

Further reading

Bell, R.P. (1959), *Acids and Bases,* Methuen, London.
Bell, R.P. (1961), *The Proton in Chemistry,* Methuen, London.
Clever, H.L. (1963), *J. Chem. Educ.,* **40**, 637, *The Hydrated Hydronium Ion.*
Prue, J.E. (1966), *Ionic Equilibria,* Pergamon, Oxford.

Electrolytic conduction

4

4.1   The significance of conductivity data

Experimental determinations of the conducting properties of electrolyte solutions are important essentially in two respects. Firstly, it is possible to study quantitatively the effects of interionic forces, degrees of dissociation and the extent of ion-pairing. Secondly, conductance values may be used to determine quantities such as solubilities of sparingly soluble salts, ionic products of self-ionizing solvents, dissociation constants of weak acids and to form the basis for conductimetric titration methods.

The resistance of a portion of an electrolyte solution may be defined in the same way as for a metallic conductor by

$$R = \rho \cdot \frac{l}{A} \tag{4.1}$$

ρ being the specific resistance or resistivity and l and A the length (m) and area (m^2) respectively of the portion of solution studied. $1/R$ is known as the conductance of the material. Of greater importance here is the reciprocal of ρ, known as the conductivity, κ i.e.,

$$\kappa = \frac{1}{\rho} = \frac{l}{RA} \tag{4.2}$$

κ has the units $\Omega^{-1}\,m^{-1}$. The term specific conductance formerly used for κ ($\Omega^{-1}\,cm^{-1}$) is now obsolete.

4.1.1   Measurement of conductivity

A Wheatstone bridge arrangement may be used to measure the resistance of a portion of a solution bounded by electrodes of fixed area held at a fixed

52

separation from each other. These electrodes are usually of platinum with a coating of finely divided platinum (platinum black) electro-deposited on their surfaces. Two complications are immediately apparent: firstly, application of a direct voltage across the electrodes is likely to cause electrolysis and the electrodes are said to become polarized; secondly, it is difficult to measure the area of the electrodes and the distance between them – maintaining these parameters at fixed values can also present some problems. To overcome the first difficulty, it is essential to use an alternating voltage source so that no significant accumulation of electrolysis products can occur at the electrodes: the changes occurring in one half-cycle being reversed in the next half-cycle. The catalytic properties of the platinum black ensure that the electrode reactions occur rapidly and stay in phase with the applied alternating voltage. The second problem is solved by determining a *cell constant* with a solution of accurately known κ. What is actually measured, of course, is the resistance R, with κ determined from

$$R = \frac{1}{\kappa} \cdot \frac{l}{A} \qquad (4.3)$$

If κ for a standard solution of a reference electrolyte is known, l/A – the cell constant – may be calculated from an observed resistance using the cell in question and the standard electrolyte. Potassium chloride is the accepted standard for which accurately determined values of κ at different concentrations and temperature in aqueous solution are available. Once the cell constant is known the conductivity of any electrolyte may be determined from its measured resistance using Equation (4.3). The essential circuit is shown in Fig. 4.1.

The variable condenser connected in parallel with the variable resistance, R_3, serves to balance the capacity effects of the conductance cell. Adjustment of C and R_3 are made until the detector indicates zero voltage difference between points 1 and 3. In this condition of bridge balance the resistance R_C may be found from the expression $R_1/R_2 = R_3/R_C$. The position of balance may be indicated by a minimum signal on an oscilloscope or by minimum sound in earphones using audio frequency alternating voltage sources.

For maximum sensitivity in measuring high conductivities a high cell constant is required. Here the cell should be of the type shown in Fig. 4.2 with small electrodes separated by a large distance. Conversely, for the measure-

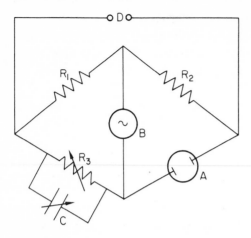

FIGURE 4.1
A.C. bridge circuit for conductivity determination.

A. Conductivity cell.
B. Oscillator (~1000 c/s). .
C. Capacitance (variable) to balance capacitance as well as resistance of conductance cell.
D. Detector (headphones or oscilloscope).

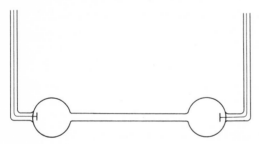

FIGURE 4.2
Conductivity cell with high cell constant. Suitable for precision measurement of high conductivities.

ment of small conductivities, l/A should be as small as possible as in Fig. 4.3. This latter design is very adaptable as a 'dip-type' cell.

4.1.2 Molar conductivity

Conductivity as a practical quantity has restricted use since it is not possible to compare values for different electrolyte concentrations owing to the sec-

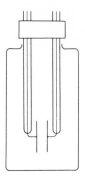

FIGURE 4.3
Conductivity cell with low cell constant.

tion of solution investigated containing different numbers of ions. Molar conductivity, given the symbol Λ, on the other hand, is defined in such a way that at any concentration the conductivity of one mole of any electrolyte may be determined.

Imagine two electrodes held at a separation of 1 m. If a solution has a concentration C mol m^{-3}, then the volume of solution containing *one* mole = $1/C$ and both electrodes would have to have this area, for a separation of 1 m, if one mole of electrolyte were to be held between them at concentration C. The molar conductivity is thus given by the conductivity, κ, multiplied by the volume which contains one mole of electrolyte, i.e. by

$$\Lambda = \frac{\kappa}{C} (\Omega^{-1} \text{ m}^2 \text{ mol}^{-1}) \qquad (4.4)$$

The previously used *equivalent conductance* was defined by

$$\Lambda_{\text{equiv}} = \frac{1000\kappa \ \Omega^{-1} \text{cm}^{-1}}{C_{\text{equiv}} \ \text{l}^{-1}}$$

It is still quite common to find conductivity and molar conductivity data given in the units Ω^{-1} cm^{-1} and Ω^{-1} cm^2 mol^{-1}, respectively. To convert molar conductivities in the units Ω^{-1} cm^2 mol^{-1} to Ω^{-1} m^2 mol^{-1} it is necessary to divide by 10^4.

4.1.3 Variation of molar conductivity with concentration

In respect of the variation of their molar conductivities with concentration,

55

strong and weak electrolytes show distinct characteristics. For strong electrolytes Kohlrausch established an empirical relationship between Λ and $\sqrt{C}$, viz.

$$\Lambda_C = \Lambda_0 - k\sqrt{C} \tag{4.5}$$

which holds up to concentrations in the region of 5 mol m^{-3}, extrapolation of a plot of Λ_C versus $\sqrt{C}$ giving Λ_0, the molar conductivity at infinite dilution.

Weak electrolytes show no such linear relationship. Their dissociation is considered to increase with increasing dilution of the solution so that the dissociation constant of a weak acid may be given as follows

$$CH_3COOH \rightleftharpoons CH_3COO^- + H^+$$
$$(1 - \alpha)C \qquad \alpha C \qquad \alpha C$$

$$K = \frac{[CH_3COO^-][H^+]}{[CH_3COOH]} = \frac{\alpha^2 C}{1 - \alpha} \tag{4.6}$$

(where α = degree of dissociation), or, if $\alpha \ll 1$,

$$K \sim \alpha^2 C \tag{4.6a}$$

The last two relations are expressions of the Ostwald dilution law. For such electrolytes, Arrhenius showed that α, the degree of dissociation, may be given quite well by the following

$$\alpha = \frac{\Lambda_C}{\Lambda_0} \tag{4.7}$$

Λ_C being the measured molar conductivity at a finite electrolyte concentration. Such an expression is obviously meaningless for strong electrolytes where ionization is complete at all concentrations. A combination of Equations (4.6) and (4.7) gives

$$K = \frac{C\Lambda_C^2}{\Lambda_0^2 \left(1 - \dfrac{\Lambda_C}{\Lambda_0}\right)} = \frac{C\Lambda_C^2}{\Lambda_0(\Lambda_0 - \Lambda_C)} \tag{4.8}$$

In Table 4.1 the essential validity of the above expressions for determining dissociation constants is demonstrated. The values of K show fairly satisfactory constancy with concentration.

Kohlrausch demonstrated that each ion of an electrolyte makes its own unique contribution to the total molar conductivity of the electrolyte which

TABLE 4.1
Dissociation constant of acetic acid at 298 K

C	$K \times 10^5$
0·001	1·851
0·005	1·851
0·010	1·846
0·050	1·771
0·100	1·551

is independent of the other ion(s). The phenomenon has expression as the law of independent migration of ions in the form

$$\Lambda_0 = \lambda_+{}^0 + \lambda_-{}^0 \qquad (4.9)$$

$\lambda_+{}^0$ and $\lambda_-{}^0$ being the ionic conductivities at infinite dilution. Equation (4.9) has been written for infinite dilution since it is only under such conditions, when ion–ion interactions are at a minimum, that the law strictly holds. It is then applicable to both strong and weak electrolytes. Its validity is demonstrated in the data of Table 4.2.

TABLE 4.2
Infinite dilution values of the molar conductivities of some electrolytes at 291 K (Ω^{-1} cm^2 mol^{-1})

Salt	Λ_0	Salt	Λ_0	$\Delta\Lambda_0$
KNO$_3$	126·3	NaNO$_3$	105·2	21·1
KCl	130·0	NaCl	108·9	21·1
$\Delta\Lambda_0$	3·7		3·7	

In quoting the Λ or Λ_0 value for a given electrolyte, it is necessary to be very careful to specify the formula unit to which the value applies. The molar conductivity of an electrolyte reflects the amount of current that it can carry, i.e. the rate of transfer of *charge* through it. When comparing Λ values for different electrolytes, it is essential to define 1 mole in all cases as the amount associated with 1 mole of unit *charges* (i.e. $6 \cdot 023 \times 10^{23}$ elementary units).

There is no problem in the case of uni-univalent electrolytes such as potassium chloride where the mole is specified as KCl, but for magnesium sulphate or sodium sulphate a mole would be specified as $\frac{1}{2}\,MgSO_4$ and $\frac{1}{2}\,Na_2 SO_4$ respectively (rather than $MgSO_4$ or $Na_2 SO_4$)

Thus, $\qquad \Lambda_0\ (MgSO_4) \quad = 2 \cdot 662 \times 10^{-2}\,\Omega^{-1}\,m^2\,mol^{-1}$

but $\qquad\qquad \Lambda_0\ (\frac{1}{2}\,MgSO_4) \ = 1 \cdot 331 \times 10^{-2}\,\Omega^{-1}\,m^2\,mol^{-1}$

and $\qquad\qquad \Lambda_0\ (Na_2 SO_4) \quad = 2 \cdot 604 \times 10^{-2}\,\Omega^{-1}\,m^2\,mol^{-1}$

but $\qquad\qquad \Lambda_0\ (\frac{1}{2}\,Na_2 SO_4) = 1 \cdot 302 \times 10^{-2}\,\Omega^{-1}\,m^2\,mol^{-1}$

One clearly has to be equally careful in the case of ion conductivities. There is, for example, no significance in comparing the values of $\lambda^0\ (Na^+)$, $\lambda^0\ (Mg^{2+})$ and $\lambda^0\ (Fe^{3+})$, but there is real significance in a comparison of $\lambda^0\ (Na^+)$, $\lambda^0\ (1/2\,Mg^{2+})$ and $\lambda^0\ (1/3\,Fe^{3+})$ in that molar values thus defined are referred in each case to the *amount of species associated with 1 mole* of electrons. Some values of limiting ion conductivities are listed in Table 4.3.

Table 4.3
Limiting molar conductivities of some ion species at 298 K

Cation	$\lambda_0^+\ (\Omega^{-1}\ m^2\ mol^{-1})$	*Anion*	$\lambda_0^-\ (\Omega^{-1}\ m^2\ mol^{-1})$
H_3O^+	$3 \cdot 499 \times 10^{-2}$	OH^-	$1 \cdot 976 \times 10^{-2}$
Na^+	$0 \cdot 502 \times 10^{-2}$	MnO_4^-	$0 \cdot 613 \times 10^{-2}$
Ag^+	$0 \cdot 619 \times 10^{-2}$	Cl^-	$0 \cdot 764 \times 10^{-2}$
$1/2\,Ca^{2+}$	$0 \cdot 595 \times 10^{-2}$	$1/2\,SO_4^{2-}$	$0 \cdot 800 \times 10^{-2}$
$1/3\,Fe^{3+}$	$0 \cdot 680 \times 10^{-2}$	$1/3\,Fe(CN)_6^{3-}$	$0 \cdot 991 \times 10^{-2}$

In the application of the Kohlrausch law, the values of molar ion conductivities used *must* refer to the quantity of ions contained in the specified amount of electrolyte.

Thus $\qquad\qquad \Lambda_0\ (\frac{1}{2}\,Na_2 SO_4) \quad = \lambda^0\ (Na^+) + \lambda^0\ (\frac{1}{2}\,SO_4^{2-})$

$$= (0 \cdot 502 + 0 \cdot 800) \times 10^{-2}\,\Omega^{-1}\,m^2\,mol^{-1}$$

$$= 1 \cdot 302 \times 10^{-2}\,\Omega^{-1}\,m^2\,mol^{-1}$$

It is, of course, equally true to write

$$\Lambda_0 \ (Na_2SO_4) \quad = \lambda^0 \ (2Na^+) + \lambda^0 \ (SO_4^{2-})$$
$$= (1 \cdot 004 + 1 \cdot 600) \times 10^{-2} \, \Omega^{-1} m^2 \ mol^{-1}$$
$$= 2 \cdot 604 \times 10^{-2} \, \Omega^{-1} m^2 \ mol^{-1}$$

A more general form of the Kohlrausch law is thus seen to be

$$\Lambda_0 \ (electrolyte) = \nu_+ \, \lambda_+^0 + \nu_- \, \lambda_-^0 \qquad (4.10)$$

where ν_+, ν_- are the numbers of moles of cation and anion, respectively, to which 1 mole of the electrolyte gives rise in solution.

4.2 Conductivity and ionic speeds

Since the conductivity of an electrolyte is a measure of the current it can carry, and therefore of the rate of charge transfer, it is also a function of the rate with which the constituent ions carry their charge through a solution. This rate depends upon the concentration and valency of the ions as well as upon their speeds.

Movement of ions through a solution is induced by the imposition of an electric field — a consequence of the applied potential between the electrodes. The electric field force experienced by an ion causes it to accelerate. This acceleration, however, is opposed by the *retarding* forces of the asymmetry and electrophoretic effects as well as by the solvent viscosity, so that an ion ultimately moves with a uniform velocity determined by a balance of these opposing forces. For a *strong* electrolyte at concentration c, giving rise to cations with charge z_+ at concentration c_+ and anions with charge z_- at concentration c_-, the amount of charge crossing *unit area* of solution in unit time is given by

$$c_+ v_+ z_+ F + c_- v_- z_- F = I_+ + I_- = I \qquad (4.11)$$

where I is the current density, I_+, I_- are the current density contributions from cation and anion while v_+ v_- are the *speeds* of the two ionic species.

In the case of a *weak* electrolyte, where each molecule produces ν_+ cations and ν_- anions, with a degree of ionization α, then

59

$$c_+ = \alpha v_+ c \text{ and } c_- = \alpha v_- c$$

Substitution for c_+, c_- into Equation (4.11) gives

$$I = \alpha c F (v_+ v_+ z_+ + v_- v_- z_-) \tag{4.12}$$

Now, the speeds with which ions move are linear functions of the field strength, $\vec{F}$, so that we may write,

$$v_+ = u_+ \vec{F} \text{ and } v_- = u_- \vec{F} \tag{4.13}$$

Here the proportionality constants u_+, u_- are the mobilities of the respective ionic species, i.e. their *speeds* under a unit field strength at a *specified* concentration of electrolyte. Values of u_+, u_- *vary with concentration.*

Introducing the expressions for v_+, v_- from Equations (4.13) into Equation (4.12) gives

$$I = \alpha c F \vec{F} (v_+ u_+ z_+ + v_- u_- z_-) \tag{4.14}$$

Equation (4.14) may further be expressed in terms of the conductivity, κ, or molar conductivity, Λ, since,

$$\kappa = \frac{l}{RA} \quad \text{(see Equation (4.2))}$$

$$= \frac{li}{EA} \quad \left(\text{substituting } \frac{1}{R} = \frac{i}{E} \text{ by Ohm's law, where}\right.$$
$$i = \text{current and } E = \text{potential})$$

or, $\quad \kappa = \dfrac{i/A}{E/l} \quad$ (where A = area of solution across which ions are considered to be moving)

$$\therefore \ \kappa = \frac{I}{\vec{F}} \tag{4.15}$$

Therefore, in terms of Equation (4.14), the conductivity κ_c at concentration c may be expressed as

$$\kappa_c = \frac{I}{\overrightarrow{F}} = \alpha c F \left(\nu_+ u_+ z_+ + \nu_- u_- z_- \right)$$

Or,
$$\Lambda_c = \frac{\kappa_c}{c} = \alpha F \left(\nu_+ u_+ z_+ + \nu_- u_- z_- \right) \qquad (4.16)$$

Now, at infinite dilution $\alpha = 1$ and u_+, u_- will reach limiting values u_+^0, u_-^0; Equation (4.16) then becomes

$$\Lambda_0 = F \left(\nu_+ u_+^0 z_+ + \nu_- u_-^0 z_- \right) \qquad (4.17)$$

and since

$$\Lambda_0 = \nu_+ \lambda_+^0 + \nu_- \lambda_-^0 \quad \text{(Equation (4.10))}$$

$$\Lambda_0 = \nu_+ u_+^0 z_+ F + \nu_- u_-^0 z_- F \qquad (4.18)$$

where
$$\lambda_+^0 = u_+^0 z_+ F \text{ and } \lambda_-^0 = u_-^0 z_- F \qquad (4.19)$$

Equations (4.17), (4.18), (4.19) are clearly valid for both strong and weak electrolytes at infinite dilution.

It should be noted with caution that some workers have used the term 'mobility' in place of molar ion conductivity. Such practice is misleading and should be avoided; the distinction between molar ion conductivity, *as a measure of the amount of current that an ion can carry,* and mobility, *which is a speed in a field of unit potential gradient,* should be clearly understood.

Evidently Equation (4.19) enables us to calculate the speeds with which ions move under the influence of an applied field when their limiting molar conductivities are known.

Consider the case of a singly charged cation for which

$$\lambda_+^0 = 0 \cdot 5 \times 10^{-2} \ \Omega^{-1} \ m^2 \ mol^{-1}.$$

$$u_+^0 = \frac{\lambda_+^0}{F} = \frac{0 \cdot 5 \times 10^{-2} \ \Omega^{-1} \ m^2 \ mol^{-1}}{96\,500 \ C \ mol^{-1}}$$

$$= 5 \cdot 2 \times 10^{-8} \ \frac{\Omega^{-1} \ m^2}{As}$$

$$= 5 \cdot 2 \times 10^{-8} \frac{m^2}{Vs}$$

$$= 5 \cdot 2 \times 10^{-8} \frac{ms^{-1}}{Vm^{-1}}$$

i.e. at infinite dilution the cation moves with a speed of $5 \cdot 2 \times 10^{-8}$ ms^{-1} in a potential gradient of $1V$ m^{-1}. Or, as the mobility would more usually be expressed,

$$u_+^0 = 5 \cdot 2 \times 10^{-8} \ m^2 \ s^{-1} \ V^{-1}$$

A table of ion mobilities is given below (Table 4.4). It is seen that H_3O^+ and OH^- ions in aqueous solution are exceptional in having extremely high mobilities. In view of what has become known about the extent of association of water molecules ('iceberg' structures) in recent years, such large values cannot

TABLE 4.4
Ion mobilities at 298 K in aqueous solution

Ion	u^0 (m^2 s^{-1} V^{-1})
H_3O^+	$36 \cdot 3 \times 10^{-8}$
OH^-	$20 \cdot 5 \times 10^{-8}$
Li^+	$4 \cdot 0 \times 10^{-8}$
Na^+	$5 \cdot 2 \times 10^{-8}$
K^+	$7 \cdot 6 \times 10^{-8}$
Ag^+	$6 \cdot 4 \times 10^{-8}$
Mg^{2+}	$5 \cdot 5 \times 10^{-8}$
Zn^{2+}	$5 \cdot 5 \times 10^{-8}$
Cl^-	$7 \cdot 9 \times 10^{-8}$
Br^-	$8 \cdot 1 \times 10^{-8}$
NO_3^-	$7 \cdot 4 \times 10^{-8}$
SO_4^{2-}	$8 \cdot 3 \times 10^{-8}$

be accounted for on the basis of the independent migration of H_3O^+ and OH^- species. In fact, a somewhat unique transport mechanism operates whereby protons are exchanged between neighbouring solvent molecules producing movement of charge and causing continuous destruction and re-formation of the species. A very similar mechanism operates in the case of $H_3SO_4^+$ and HSO_4^- in systems where concentrated sulphuric acid is used as solvent. For the other ions listed it is to be noted that the speeds are very small indeed, even in the extreme condition of infinite dilution when they can move unencumbered by other ions. It follows that electrical migration must be interpreted as a very slow drift of ions towards electrodes superimposed on their much more rapid thermal motions.

4.3   Relationships between molar conductivity and concentration

Under this heading there are three classes of behaviour that must be distinguished. In the case of strong, completely dissociated electrolytes any variation of conductivity with concentration can be traced to the varying interaction between ions as their proximity is varied by concentration changes. For weak, incompletely dissociated electrolytes changes in conductivity may be expected to occur as their degree of dissociation is forced to increase by increasing dilution. We have already briefly considered the conditions under which the ions deriving from strong electrolytes may associate into ion pairs. Since such associations reduce the effective number of conducting species, occurrence of such phenomena may be expected to reduce the conductivity below values which would be obtained were all the ions to be unassociated.

4.3.1   *Strong completely dissociated electrolytes*

We have already discussed qualitatively the *relaxation* and *electrophoretic* effects which retard the motion of ions, surrounded by their ion atmospheres, through a solution. Such effects will show themselves at the experimental level in conductivity measurements. For the ion conductivity λ_i of an ion species in a very dilute solution of a strong electrolyte, Onsager derived the expression

$$\lambda_i = \lambda^0 - \left(\frac{8\pi N\epsilon^2}{1000\varepsilon kT}\right)^{1/2} \left(\frac{z_+z_-}{3\varepsilon kT} \frac{\lambda^0 q}{(1 + \sqrt{q})} + \frac{F^2 z_i}{6\pi\eta N}\right)\left(\frac{|z_+| + |z_-|}{2}\right) C^{1/2}$$

$$(4.20)$$

where

$$q = \frac{z_+ z_-(\lambda_+{}^0 + \lambda_-{}^0)}{(|z_+| + |z_-|)(|z_+|\lambda_-{}^0 + |z_-|\lambda_+{}^0)} \quad (4.21)$$

When appropriate numerical values for universal constants are inserted, Equation (4.20) becomes

$$\lambda_i = \lambda^0 - \left[\frac{2\cdot8 \times 10^6 |z_+ z_-|q}{(\varepsilon T)^{3/2}(1+\sqrt{q})}\lambda^0 + \frac{41\cdot25 z_i}{\eta(\varepsilon T)^{1/2}}\right]\left(\frac{|z_+| + |z_-|}{2}\right)^{1/2} C^{1/2}$$
$$(4.22)$$

For a completely dissociated electrolyte the addition of two such terms, one for cationic and the other for anionic species, gives the molar conductivity by the Kohlrausch principle

$$\Lambda_C = \Lambda_0 - \left[\frac{2\cdot8 \times 10^6 |z_+ z_-|q}{(\varepsilon T)^{3/2}(1+\sqrt{q})}\Lambda_0 + \frac{41\cdot25(|z_+| + |z_-|)}{\eta(\varepsilon T)^{1/2}}\right]$$
$$\times \left(\frac{|z_+| + |z_-|}{2}\right)^{1/2} C^{1/2} \quad (4.23)$$

Or,

$$\Lambda_C = \Lambda_0 - (A\Lambda_0 + B)C^{1/2} \quad (4.24)$$

Equation (4.24) is of the same form as the empirical square root law (Equation (4.5)) found by Kohlrausch

For a symmetrical electrolyte $|z_+| = |z_-|$ and $q = 0\cdot5$, so that, for water as solvent, Equation (4.23) may be written in the form

$$\Lambda_C = \Lambda_0 - [0\cdot23\Lambda_0 + 60\cdot22]C^{1/2} \quad (4.25)$$

using $\varepsilon = 80$, $\eta = 0\cdot0089$ poise and $T = 298$ K.

In Fig. 4.4 are shown examples of the variation of experimentally determined Λ_C values as a function of $C^{1/2}$ for 1 : 1 electrolytes. The Onsager relation is a limiting one in that it only holds good for 1 : 1 electrolytes at concentrations less than $0\cdot001$ M, deviations occurring as shown at higher concentrations due to the neglect of higher terms in the limiting Onsager

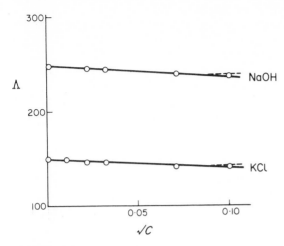

FIGURE 4.4
Variation of molar conductivity, Λ, with $\sqrt{C}$ for 1 : 1 electrolytes. Up to $\sqrt{C} \sim 0\cdot10$ the graphs are linear and have approximately the Onsager slope.

equation. Deviations for electrolytes with higher valency products occur at even lower concentrations. Electrolytes with a valency product equal to or greater than 4 show marked *negative* deviations. These are attributed to ion association and are to be distinguished from positive deviations associated with shortcomings of the Onsager equation.

Rearrangement of Equation (4.22) gives

$$\Lambda_0 = \frac{\Lambda + BC^{1/2}}{1 - AC^{1/2}} \tag{4.26}$$

Shedlovsky observed that the value of Λ_0 as calculated from Equation (4.26) was not constant, but showed almost linear variation with concentration. The linear extrapolation function

$$\Lambda_0' = \frac{(\Lambda + B\sqrt{C})}{(1 - A\sqrt{C})}$$

when plotted against concentration yields a further value of Λ_0 when extrapolated to zero concentration. This value can be defined in terms of an empirical relationship

65

$$\Lambda_0 = \frac{(\Lambda + B\sqrt{C})}{(1 - A\sqrt{C})} - bC \qquad (4.27)$$

where b is an empirical constant.

Rearrangement of Equation (4.27) yields

$$\Lambda = \Lambda_0 - (A\Lambda_0 + B)\sqrt{C} + bC(1 - A\sqrt{C}) \qquad (4.28)$$

This equation holds good for a number of electrolytes up to a concentration of 0·1 M.

In conclusion, we can see that in an *ideal* solution of a strong electrolyte Λ is independent of concentration. An approach to this condition is made in very dilute solution as seen in the portion BC of the schematic graph of Λ

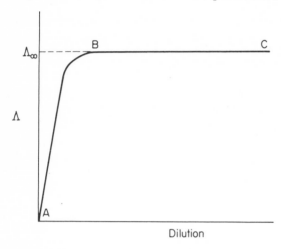

FIGURE 4.5
Schematic plot of Λ versus dilution for a strong, completely dissociated electrolyte.

AB. Extreme departure from ideality as ions interact very significantly with one another.
BC. An approach to ideal behaviour in very dilute solution in which ions interact negligibly.

versus dilution given in Fig. 4.5. Over the region AB extreme departures from ideality occur and, with increasing concentration, ion–ion and ion–solvent interactions become more and more significant. Over this region we may define a so-called conductivity coefficient g_Λ by

$$\frac{\Lambda}{\Lambda_0} = g_\Lambda \qquad (4.29)$$

4.3.2 Weak incompletely dissociated electrolytes

Experimental use of Equations (4.5) and (4.7) from the Arrhenius theory do make possible the determination of dissociation constants even though both equations are based upon erroneous assumptions. Ions, even in dilute solution, do not behave as ideal solutes and their conductivities are functions of concentration. The reasons that equilibrium constants determined by the Arrhenius equations are fairly good are that, firstly, interactions between ions are less numerous than for a strong electrolyte and secondly, and more important, corrections to α by the use of the Onsager equation and introduction of activity coefficients from the Debye–Hückel theory almost compensate one another. The Onsager equation in the case of a weak electrolyte becomes

$$\Lambda_C = \alpha[\Lambda_0 - (A\Lambda_0 + B)\sqrt{(\alpha C)}] \tag{4.30}$$

and Equation (4.29) now takes the form

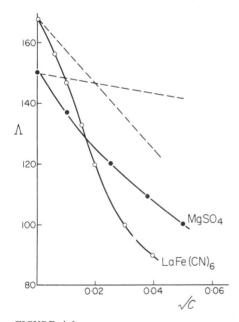

FIGURE 4.6
Deviations from the Onsager equation, shown by electrolytes with valency product 4 and 6, indicating ion-pairing. The dotted lines are the Onsager slopes.

$$\frac{\Lambda}{\Lambda_0} = \alpha g_\Lambda \tag{4.31}$$

which may be regarded as the precise form of Equation (4.7).

4.3.3 Electrolyte systems showing ion pairing

We have seen that deviations from the Onsager equation in its limiting form occur for uni-univalent electrolytes at higher concentrations where observed molar conductivities are somewhat *higher* than predicted so that the slope of the Λ versus $C^{1/2}$ graph is somewhat lower than the theoretical Onsager slope. Electrolytes with a valency product less than 4 show fair to good agreement with the Onsager equation at low concentrations, although the upper concentration limit at which deviation begins to occur becomes progressively lower as the valency product increases. When this product is greater than 4 it is no longer possible to perform experiments at the extremely high dilutions where the Onsager equation might be expected to hold. Even for the lowest concentrations accessible the deviations are now extreme (Fig. 4.6).

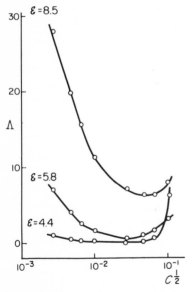

FIGURE 4.7
Plots of molar conductivity versus $C^{1/2}$ for tetraisoamylammonium nitrate at various values of dielectric constant.

However, such deviations occur in the opposite sense to those obtained with low valency product electrolytes, i.e. observed conductivities are now substantially lower than those predicted. Such deviations indicate a drastic reduction in the number of conducting species in solution, i.e. association to form ion-pairs has taken place. Such deviations become more marked in solvents of low dielectric constant. In such cases the molar conductivity versus $C^{1/2}$ graph may show a minimum (Fig. 4.7) and this is attributed to the formation of triple ions which, unlike ion-pairs, carry a net charge. The formation of ion pairs removes two charged species from solution for each association which occurs and the conductivity must fall as this process increases in importance. At some stage further association between an ion-pair and a further ion may be expected. Since this gives rise to a charged species, which can contribute to the conductivity, the decrease in conductivity is observed to proceed less rapidly and to reach a minimum value when the contributions of the double and triple ions to the total conductivity are equal. As the concentration is increased still further more triple ions than ion-pairs are formed and the conductivity rises.

4.4 Conductivity at high field strengths and high frequency of alternation of the field

In normal fields of the order of a few volts per cm, conductivities show no measurable variation with field. Wien, however, using fields of the order of 100 kV cm^{-1} observed an increase in conductivity whose magnitude is a function of both the concentration and the charge on the ions of the electrolyte. For a given concentration of a particular electrolyte, a limiting value of conductivity is reached at higher field strengths.

Under the influence of such high field strengths, the ions move very rapidly indeed (up to metres s^{-1}). Since the rearrangement time of the atmosphere about an ion is slow by comparison, the retardation of the ion's motion by the electrophoretic and relaxation effects becomes progressively smaller as the field strength becomes larger. This effect is only observed for strong electrolytes.

The conductivity of weak electrolytes, e.g. weak acids, is also increased under the influence of high fields. This *dissociation field effect,* or second Wien effect, is caused quite differently from that described for strong electrolytes. The high field in this case changes the values of the dissociation constants of weak electrolytes. For an acid dissociation

$$HA \underset{k_{-1}}{\overset{k_1}{\rightleftharpoons}} H^+ + A^-$$

where k_1, k_{-1} are the forward and backward rate constants, the dissociation constant, K_a, is given by

$$K_a = k_1/k_{-1}$$

Since the H—A bond has some electrostatic character, the acid molecule has, to a limited extent, the properties of an ion-pair. While the rate of *formation* of an ion-pair is independent of an external field, the dissociation rate is *increased*, i.e. k_1 increases relative to a constant k_{-1} with consequent increase in K_a. The equilibrium shifts to a new position corresponding to a higher concentration of H^+ and A^-.

An increase in conductivity of strong electrolytes is also observed with high-frequency fields operating at frequencies greater than 5 megacycles per second. At such frequencies, a central ion oscillates at a frequency comparable to the relaxation time of the atmosphere. The relaxation effect thus becomes smaller the greater the frequency and the conductivity rises. The electrophoretic effect remains unchanged.

4.5   Electrical migration and transport numbers

In order to determine λ_+, λ_- from measurements of the conductance of an electrolyte, it is necessary to know the fraction of the total current passed which is carried by each ion type. Such fractions are known as *transport numbers, t.* By definition, the *sum* of the transport numbers of all ion species in an electrolyte solution is *unity*.

Equation (4.11) gave the anion and cation current density contributions,

$$I_+ = c_+ \, v_+ \, z_+ \, F; I_- = c_- \, v_- \, z_- \, F$$

and

$$I = I_+ + I_- = c_+ \, v_+ \, z_+ \, F + c_- \, v_- \, z_- \, F$$

So that the *fraction, t_+,* of the current density carried by the cation is

$$t_+ = \frac{I_+}{I_+ + I_-} = \frac{c_+ \, v_+ \, z_+ \, F}{F \, (c_+ \, v_+ \, z_+ + c_- v_- z_-)} \qquad (4.32)$$

For a uni-univalent electrolyte, $c_+ = c_- = c$ and $|z_+| = |z_-| = 1$, so that Equation (4.32) becomes

$$t_+ = \frac{v_+}{v_+ + v_-} \qquad (4.33)$$

Similarly, for the anion,

$$t_- = \frac{v_-}{v_+ + v_-} \qquad (4.34)$$

The concentration dependence of transport numbers is implicit in Equation (4.34) owing to the concentration dependence of ion speeds.

For a solution containing several electrolytes, the transport number of an individual species is defined similarly, viz.,

$$t_+ = \frac{v_+}{\Sigma v} \; ; t_- = \frac{v_-}{\Sigma v} \qquad (4.35)$$

From such expressions it is evident that transport number values are very much dependent on the nature and concentration of other ion species present. The greater the number of other ion species, the smaller will be the fraction of the total current carried by the ion under consideration and hence the smaller its transport number. This phenomenon is made use of in a number of electroanalytical techniques to be described later: if the transport number of a particular species can be made so small that it approaches zero, a condition has been reached where that species ceases to migrate and no current is carried by it.

Now, from Equation (4.13)

$$v_+ = u_+ \, \vec{F} \text{ and } v_- = u_- \, \vec{F}$$

so that Equation (4.32) may equally well be written

$$t_+ = \frac{c_+ u_+ z_+}{c_+ u_+ z_+ + c_- u_- z_-}$$

and since $c_+ = \alpha v_+ c$ and $c_- = \alpha v_- c$,

$$t_+ = \frac{\alpha v_+ c u_+ z_+}{\alpha v_+ c u_+ z_+ + \alpha v_- c u_- z_-}$$

$$\therefore \; t_+ = \frac{v_+ u_+ z_+}{v_+ u_+ z_+ + v_- u_- z_-}$$

Also for electroneutrality, $|v_+ z_+| = |v_- z_-|$

$$\therefore \; t_+ = \frac{u_+}{u_+ + u_-} \quad \text{and} \quad t_- = \frac{u_-}{u_+ + u_-} \tag{4.36}$$

Now $\lambda_+^0 = u_+^0 z_+ F$; $\lambda_-^0 = u_-^0 z_- F$ (see Equation (4.19)).

So that for the special case of infinite dilution,

$$t_+^0 = \frac{u_+^0}{u_+^0 + u_-^0} \; ; \; t_-^0 = \frac{u_-^0}{u_+ + u_-^0}$$

$$\therefore \; t_+^0 = \frac{\lambda_+^0 / z_+ F}{\lambda_+^0 / z_+ F + \lambda_-^0 / z_- F} \; ; \; t_-^0 = \frac{\lambda_-^0 / z_- F}{\lambda_+^0 / z_+ F + \lambda_-^0 / z_- F} \tag{4.37}$$

and remembering again that $|v_+ z_+| = |v_- z_-|$ the last relationships become

$$t_+^0 = \frac{v_+ \lambda_+^0}{v_+ \lambda_+^0 + v_- \lambda_-^0} \; ; \; t_-^0 = \frac{v_- \lambda_-^0}{v_+ \lambda_+^0 + v_- \lambda_-^0}$$

or, in terms of the modified Kohlrausch law given in Equation (4.10)

$$t_+^0 = \frac{v_+ \lambda_+^0}{\Lambda^0} \; ; \; t_-^0 = \frac{v_- \lambda_-^0}{\Lambda^0} \tag{4.38}$$

Equations (4.38) enable λ_+^0, λ_-^0 to be determined from a knowledge of t_+^0, t_-^0 and Λ^0, the transport numbers at infinite dilution being calculated by extrapolating to zero concentration a series of values obtained by measurements made over a range of electrolyte concentration.

Equations (4.38) hold for *both* strong and weak electrolytes at infinite dilution. At finite concentrations the same *form* of Equations (4.38) holds *approximately* for strong electrolytes, the quantities having values corresponding to the concentration used. In the case of a weak electrolyte the approximate relationships must include the degree of ionization corresponding to its concentration.

It is apparent from the above relationships that t_+, t_- are related by the expression

$$t_+ + t_- = 1$$

Essentially there are three methods by means of which transport numbers may be determined, viz. (i) the method due to Hittorf (of which there are several modifications), (ii) the moving boundary method (of which, again, there are several forms) and (iii) methods based on measurements of the e.m.f.'s of concentration cells. The principles of methods (i) and (ii) will be considered here, the e.m.f. determination being discussed in a later chapter dealing with the application of e.m.f. measurements.

4.5.1 Hittorf's method

In this method the cathode, anode and central portions of an electrolysis cell are made physically distinct and solutions contained within them (catholyte, anolyte and central) are analysed after controlled electrolysis for a known period of time.

Fig. 4.8 shows the Hittorf mechanism of electrolysis when using electrodes made of the metal whose cations are those of the electrolyte in solution and when Q coulombs are passed. It is seen that the concentration of the electrolyte in the central portion of the cell remains unchanged at the end of the electrolysis.

Consider an electrolyte, represented by MX, whose constituent ions are

73

M^{z+} and X^{z-} where $|z_+| = |z_-|$ (an example would be copper sulphate giving Cu^{2+} and SO_4^{2-}).

At the cathode M^{z+} ions are discharged according to

$$M^{z+} + ze \rightarrow M$$

while at the anode M dissolves,

$$M \rightarrow M^{z+} + ze$$

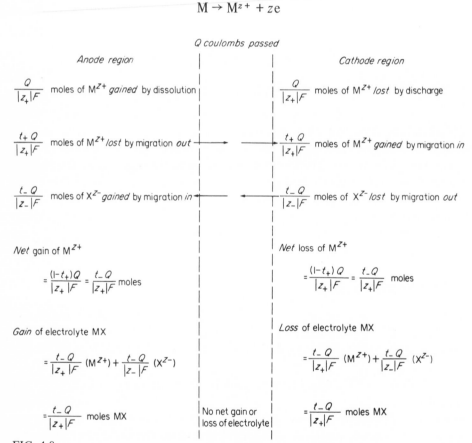

FIG. 4.8

Hittorf electrolysis mechanism for the case where the electrodes are of the metal whose cation is that of the electrolyte in solution.

As a consequence of Faraday's Laws (Chapter 1), after the passage of Q coulombs, $\dfrac{Q}{|z_+|F}$ moles of M have been deposited on the cathode surface.

Of these $\dfrac{Q}{|z_+|F}$ moles only an amount $\dfrac{t_+ Q}{|z_+|F}$ is provided by the migration process. The remainder must be provided by electrolyte close to the cathode surface. Most of the species M^{z+} will thus be stripped out of the immediate vicinity of the cathode soon after electrolysis is started.

A concentration gradient will now be set up between the solution at the surface of the cathode and regions of the solution further away. Across this gradient M^{z+} and X^{z-} ions will diffuse and, by the time Q coulombs have passed, $\dfrac{t_- Q}{|z_+|F}$ moles of M^{z+} will have been provided by diffusion, and discharged as M, to make up the total of $\dfrac{Q}{|z_+|F}$ moles of M deposited.

When a steady current flows, the concentration gradient at the electrode surface automatically adjusts itself to maintain just the correct rate of diffusion. Diffusion of *both* ion species of the electrolyte ensures that there is always sufficient of the anion being provided in this region so that the rate of *migration* of the anion away from the cathode is maintained. It is seen from Fig. 4.8 that a net *loss* of $\dfrac{t_- Q}{|z_+|F}$ moles of electrolyte occurs in the catholyte solution.

Similar arguments apply to the anode region. After the passage of Q coulombs, $\dfrac{Q}{|z_+|F}$ moles of M^{z+} have dissolved from the anode, of which $\dfrac{t_+ Q}{|z_+|F}$ migrate *out*, leaving a net *gain* of $\dfrac{t_- Q}{|z_+|F}$ moles of M^{z+} in the anolyte. This is complemented by the migration into the anolyte of $\dfrac{t_- Q}{|z_-|F}$ moles of X^{z-}. Thus a net *gain* of $\dfrac{t_- Q}{|z_+|F}$ moles of electrolyte occurs in the anolyte solution.

As to the central portion, whatever it has gained from the anode region it has donated to the cathode region and vice versa. It thus experiences neither a net gain nor a net loss of electrolyte during the course of the electrolysis unless this is so prolonged that the diffusion processes, referred to above, extend so far out from the electrode surfaces that they become significant here and invalidate the calculations.

It is important to note that for the above case, in which it is the *cations* which react at the electrodes, the losses and gains in both electrode regions are functions of the transport number of the *anion*. It is evident that the transport number of the cation cannot be determined independently but must be calculated from the expression

$$t_+ + t_- = 1$$

For the case where the electrolyte is of a more general type whose ions are dispersed in solution according to

$$M_{\nu_+} X_{\nu_-} \rightarrow \nu_+ M^{z+} + \nu_- X^{z-}$$

then the respective gain and loss of electrolyte in anolyte and catholyte is again given by,

$$\frac{t_- Q}{|z_+|F}(M^{z+}) + \frac{t_- Q}{|z_-|F}(X^{z-})$$

Here, however,
$$z_+ \neq z_-$$

but rather
$$\nu_+ z_+ = \nu_- z_-$$

i.e., the gain and loss become

$$\frac{t_- Q}{|z_+|F}(M^{z+}) + \frac{\nu_-}{\nu_+} \cdot \frac{t_- Q}{|z_+|F} = \frac{t_- Q}{|z_+|F} \text{ moles of } M_{\nu_+} X_{\nu_-}$$

For example, in the case of a cupric halide, CuX_2 for which $z_+ = 2, z_- = 1$ and $\nu_+ = 1, \nu_- = 2$, the gain and loss is

$$\frac{t_- Q}{2F}(Cu^{2+}) + \frac{2t_- Q}{2F}(X^-) = \frac{t_- Q}{2F}(CuX_2)$$

Electrolysis processes may not always be as simple as this and caution must be exercised in calculating transport numbers in that it is necessary to have firm prior knowledge of precisely what electrode reactions occur. For

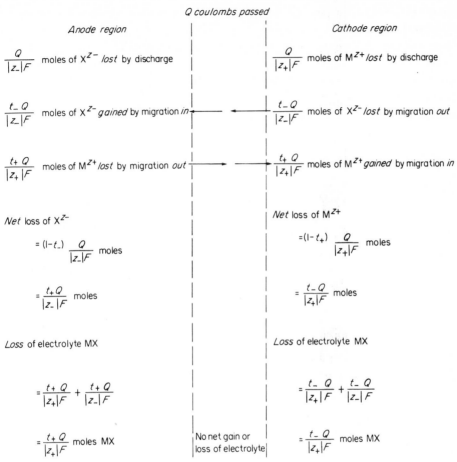

Q coulombs passed

Anode region

Cathode region

$\dfrac{Q}{|z_-|F}$ moles of X^{z-} *lost* by discharge

$\dfrac{Q}{|z_+|F}$ moles of M^{z+} *lost* by discharge

$\dfrac{t_-Q}{|z_-|F}$ moles of X^{z-} *gained* by migration *in*

$\dfrac{t_-Q}{|z_-|F}$ moles of X^{z-} *lost* by migration *out*

$\dfrac{t_+Q}{|z_+|F}$ moles of M^{z+} *lost* by migration *out*

$\dfrac{t_+Q}{|z_+|F}$ moles of M^{z+} *gained* by migration *in*

Net loss of X^{z-}

$= (1-t_-)\dfrac{Q}{|z_-|F}$ moles

$= \dfrac{t_+Q}{|z_-|F}$ moles

Net loss of M^{z+}

$= (1-t_+)\dfrac{Q}{|z_+|F}$ moles

$= \dfrac{t_-Q}{|z_+|F}$ moles

Loss of electrolyte MX

$= \dfrac{t_+Q}{|z_+|F} + \dfrac{t_+Q}{|z_-|F}$

$= \dfrac{t_+Q}{|z_+|F}$ moles MX

Loss of electrolyte MX

$= \dfrac{t_-Q}{|z_+|F} + \dfrac{t_-Q}{|z_-|F}$

$= \dfrac{t_-Q}{|z_+|F}$ moles MX

No net gain or loss of electrolyte

FIG. 4.9
Hittorf electrolysis mechanism for the case in which anion and cation are discharged at inert electrodes.

instance, for the electrolysis of metal salts with inert electrodes, such as platinum, hydrogen and not the metal cation may be discharged; similarly oxygen may be discharged in preference to the anion. Even if the electrolyte anion and cation are discharged, the net result using inert electrodes will be quite different from the case considered above. The mechanism in this case is shown in Fig. 4.9. Here it is seen that there is a net *loss* of electrolyte from both anode and cathode regions. Again, however, no gain or loss occurs in the central region.

For this case at the cathode M^{z+} cations are discharged,

$$M^{z+} + ze \rightarrow M$$

while at the anode X^{z-} anions are discharged

$$X^{z-} \rightarrow X + ze$$

·The essential experimental circuit for Hittorf's method is shown in Fig. 4.10. A current of 10–20 mA is passed for 1–2 hours. Smaller currents passed for longer times encourage the undesirable diffusion into the central compartment. After electrolysis, samples of solution from anode and/or cathode compartment are withdrawn and analysed. It is also advisable to analyse a sample of solution from the central compartment to check that the composition in this region has, in fact, remained unchanged.

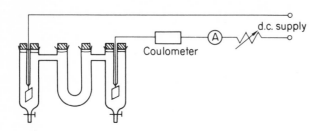

FIGURE 4.10
Essential experimental circuit for Hittorf determination of transport numbers.

It is most important that concentrations of the compartments be referred to a given weight of solvent, since concentration changes in the electrolyte solution are associated with volume changes. This is due to the fact that ionic species are hydrated and carry their hydration shells with them during their movements through a solution during electrolysis. Suppose that a given weight of solvent contains n_0 moles of a cation species initially and n after electrolysis. If n_e is the number of moles deposited cathodically (determined by the series coulometer), $t_+ n_e$ is the number added to the cathode region by migration. Thus,

$$n - n_0 = n_e - t_+ n_e$$

therefore,

$$t_+ = \frac{n_e + n_0 - n}{n_e} \tag{4.39}$$

Hittorf's method provides an excellent demonstration of the nature of electrolysis processes. On the practical level, however, it has obvious drawbacks, not least of which is the usually low precision with which the small concentration changes may be determined.

4.5.2 Moving boundary methods

Such methods represent direct applications of Equations (4.33) and (4.34) whereby transport numbers are related to the speeds with which ions move. Moving boundary techniques are based upon the observed rate of movement, under the influence of an applied e.m.f., of a sharp boundary between solutions of two different electrolytes having an anion or cation in common. Measurement of the rate of movement of a *sharp* boundary presents few problems, since, even if the solutions do not differ in colour, the difference

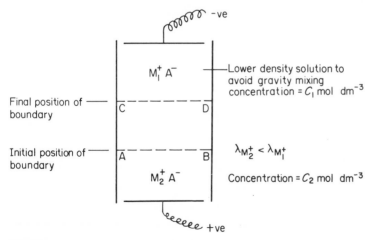

FIGURE 4.11
Principle of moving boundary method.

in their refractive indices makes the boundary between them easily distinguishable. A schematic diagram of the relation between two such solutions is shown in Fig. 4.11 for the determination of the transport number of a cation. For anion transport numbers, two electrolytes with a common cation are used. If the transport number of M_1^+ is required, $M_2^+X^-$ is referred to as the indicator electrolyte, M_1^+ being sometimes referred to as the leading ion. It is necessary for this latter ion to have a higher conductivity than M_2^+.

Let us suppose that the boundary moves from AB to CD when a quantity it coulombs of electricity are passed; let the volume swept out by the boundary be V. Thus, in the volume bounded by AB and CD, the $M_1^+X^-$ initially present is completely replaced by $M_2^+X^-$ after the passage of it coulombs. Or, C_1VF charges pass through a section of the tube in time t. This in turn must be equal to the fraction t_1^+it of the quantity of electricity passed. Therefore,

$$t_1^+ = \frac{C_1VF}{it} \tag{4.40}$$

Apart from the density and conductivity conditions indicated in Fig. 4.11, there is a particular value of the ratio C_1/C_2 necessary for the boundary to remain sharp. This may be shown as follows: suppose that the boundary moves from AB to CD on the passage of 1 faraday, so that the quantity of M_1^+ transported across the boundary is t_1^+ moles. Since this was originally contained in a volume V, it follows that

$$t_1^+ = C_1V \tag{4.41}$$

Similarly, for the indicator electrolyte,

$$t_2^+ = C_2V \tag{4.42}$$

Or, combining Equations (4.41) and (4.42)

$$\frac{C_2}{C_1} = \frac{t_2^+}{t_1^+} \tag{4.43}$$

It appears from this last equation that only by accurate fore-knowledge of t_2^+/t_1^+ could the correct value of C_2 be decided. In practice it is only found necessary for Equation (4.43) to hold within about 10%. Since the indicator solution is chosen to have a lower conductivity than that of the electrolyte under study, the field gradients must differ in the two solutions if the ions M_1^+ and M_2^+ are to move at the *same speed* and maintain a sharp boundary. Since $\lambda_{M_2^+} < \lambda_{M_1^+}$, the potential gradient (for a given current) is steeper in the indicator solution than in the leading solution. If M_1^+ ions tended to lag behind the boundary into the indicator solution, they would immediately be accelerated by the steeper potential gradient towards the boundary. Similarly, if M_2^+ ions tended to move in front of the boundary, the smaller potential gradient would serve to slow them down (Fig. 4.12).

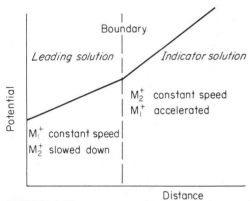

FIGURE 4.12
Conditions for maintenance of a sharp boundary.

The simplest use of the moving boundary method is that in which an *autogenic* boundary is formed, i.e., one formed spontaneously at the start of an electrolysis. The principles are shown in Fig. 4.13. The cathode is chosen as appropriate to the electrolyte to be studied – if the transport number of a metal ion M^+ is to be determined, an electrolyte MX would be used, using a cathode of metal M. The anode is usually made of copper or cadmium. On application of a potential the anode dissolves and a solution of CuX_2 or CdX_2 is formed near its surface. This comprises the indicator solution, the boundary between MX and CuX_2 or CdX_2 being followed in order to obtain the transport number of M^+ by Equation (4.40).

4.5.3 Interpretation and application of transport numbers
In section 4.5.1 it was pointed out how necessary it is to know and under-

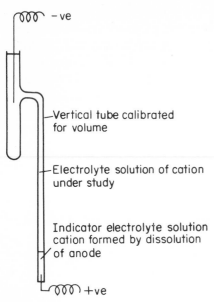

−ve

Vertical tube calibrated
for volume

Electrolyte solution of cation
under study

Indicator electrolyte solution
cation formed by dissolution
of anode

+ve

FIG. 4.13
The formation of an autogenic boundary.

stand the electrode process which occurs at the anode and cathode during
transport number measurements so that one is quite sure which ion it is for
which a certain value is determined. One must also pay strict attention to the
way in which an electrolyte may ionize and the forms in which the ions are
present in solution under given conditions. In this way experimental results
which at first sight appear unrealistic may often be explained rationally. The
cadmium ion shows a transport number of about 0·4 in very dilute solutions
of cadmium iodide. With progressively higher electrolyte concentrations,
however, the value drops sharply *below* 0·4, passes through zero and finally
attains negative values. At the same time the transport number of the iodide
ion apparently increases beyond 0·6, passes through, and eventually exceeds,
unity.

The above observations are easily explained when the nature of the ions
present in more concentrated solutions of cadmium iodide is understood. In
such solutions this electrolyte exists largely as Cd^{2+}, and CdI_4^{2-}, i.e. as the
simple cadmium ion with a double charge and as a doubly charged anionic

complexion. This latter will obviously migrate in a direction opposite to that of the simple ion. The fact that measured cadmium transport numbers approach negative values indicates that the conductivity of the complexed form is greater than that of the uncomplexed (aquo) form so that a *net loss* of cadmium occurs at the cathode.

A more fundamental use of transport numbers is in the determination of ion conductivities from measurements of conductivities of electrolytes; an ion conductivity being a fraction t_+ of the observed value for the electrolyte. In order to obtain infinite dilution values of ion conductivities, molar conductivities and transport numbers also have to be obtained by extrapolation to these conditions. In some cases this process may be unreliable. Once, however, the conductivity of a given ion is reliably obtained, it is possible to obtain those of any oppositely charged partner in a variety of electrolytes by subtraction.

4.6 Applications of conductivity measurements

4.6.1 Determination of molar conductivities at infinite dilution

For strong electrolytes, Λ_0 may be determined from observed molar conductivities over a range of electrolyte concentration. These values are then extrapolated to zero concentration in accordance with the Onsager equation. It is important that the range of concentration should be well within the limits for the Onsager equation to hold. If this is not the case, then extended forms of the equation must be used.

In the case of weak electrolytes, Λ_0 may be determined either from a knowledge of the dissociation constant of the electrolyte or by making use of the Kohlrausch independent migration relation. For example, Λ_0 for acetic acid may be calculated from experimentally determined values of Λ_0 for hydrochloric acid, sodium acetate and sodium chloride – all strong electrolytes. From the Kohlrausch relation we may write

$$
\begin{align}
_{HCl}\Lambda_0 &= (\lambda_{H^+})^0 + (\lambda_{Cl^-})^0 \quad &\text{(i)} \\
_{NaAc}\Lambda_0 &= (\lambda_{Na^+})^0 + (\lambda_{Ac^-})^0 \quad &\text{(ii)} \\
_{NaCl}\Lambda_0 &= (\lambda_{Na^+})^0 + (\lambda_{Cl^-})^0 \quad &\text{(iii)}
\end{align}
\tag{4.44}
$$

Addition of (i) and (ii) followed by subtraction of (iii) gives

$$(_{HCl}\Lambda_0 + {}_{NaAc}\Lambda_0) - {}_{NaCl}\Lambda_0 = (\lambda_{H^+})^0 + (\lambda_{Ac^-})^0 = {}_{HAc}\Lambda_0 \quad (4.45)$$

4.6.2 Solubilities of sparingly soluble salts

The conductivity of a saturated solution of a sparingly soluble salt may be found by subtracting from the observed value in water the conductivity of water itself. For such low concentrations of electrolyte the value for water, however pure, will now be significant, the small number of ions produced by the electrolyte giving a conductance of the same order of magnitude as water; e.g.,

κ for AgCl(saturated) at 298 K $\sim$ 3·4 x 10^{-6} ohm^{-1} cm^{-1}

κ for H_2O at 298 K $\sim$ 1·6 x 10^{-6} ohm^{-1} cm^{-1}

therefore,

$$\kappa = \kappa_{soln} - \kappa_{solvent}$$

The molar conductivity of the saturated solution of the salt, Λ_S, is given by

$$\Lambda_S = \frac{\kappa}{C} \quad (\text{see } 4.4)$$

Since very little of such an electrolyte will appear in solution, Λ_S may be taken as approximating very closely to Λ_0, i.e. an infinitely dilute solution of ions is effectively formed. Thus,

$$C = \frac{\kappa}{\Lambda_0} = \frac{\kappa}{(\lambda_+)^0 + (\lambda_-)^0} \quad (4.46)$$

Hence, knowing κ and Λ_0, C may be found.

4.6.3 The ionic product of self-ionizing solvents

For water, which we have seen ionizes according to $H_2O + H_2O \rightleftharpoons H_3O^+ + OH^-$,

$$K_W = [H_3O^+][OH^-]$$

It is necessary to determine κ for very pure water. Then, knowing the ion conductivities for water at infinite dilution

$$C = [H_3O^+] = [OH^-] = \frac{\kappa}{(\lambda_{H^+})^0 + (\lambda_{OH^-})^0} \quad (4.47)$$

Hence C may be found and $K_W = C^2$.

4.6.4 Dissociation constants of weak electrolytes, e.g. weak acids

Dissociation constants may be determined from conductance data by the use of Equation (4.8) which, on rearrangement, gives

$$C\Lambda_C = K_a \frac{\Lambda_0^2}{\Lambda_C}\left(1 - \frac{\Lambda_C}{\Lambda_0}\right)$$

$$= K_a\left(\frac{\Lambda_0^2}{\Lambda_C} - \Lambda_0\right)$$

A plot of $C\Lambda_C$ versus $1/\Lambda_C$ gives a straight line of slope $K_a\Lambda_0^2$ and intercept $-K_a\Lambda_0$ from both of which K_a is determinable.

In order to determine the thermodynamic constant K_a^T it is necessary to determine K_a at different low concentrations and to obtain corresponding values of the degree of dissociation, α. From Equation (2.40)

$$\log K_a^T = \log K_a - 2A\sqrt{I}$$

A being the Debye–Hückel constant for water as solvent, and for a weak acid HA

$$I = \tfrac{1}{2}([H^+] + [A^-]) \quad \text{and} \quad [H^+] = [A^-] = \alpha C$$

therefore,

$$I = \alpha C$$

therefore,

$$\log K_a^T = \log K_a - 2A\sqrt{(\alpha C)} \qquad (4.48)$$

where K_a^T is the true thermodynamic dissociation constant of the acid, a plot of $\log K_a$ versus $\sqrt{(\alpha C)}$ giving a straight line of intercept $\log K_a^T$.

4.6.5 Conductimetric titrations

Variations of conductivity may be used to follow the courses of acid/base and precipitation reactions. A drawback of the latter is the possible contamination of the electrodes by the precipitate formed. A grave disadvantage of any conductivity-based titration is its non-applicability in the presence of high concentrations of electrolyte species other than those required to be determined. This is in contrast to many other electroanalytical techniques where such electrolytes not only do not interfere, but offer distinct advantages.

Conductimetric titration curves for acid–base reactions depend upon the relative strengths of the acids and bases used. In order to maintain straight-line variations of conductivity, it is best to use a titrant concentration considerably greater than that of titrand.

(1) Titration of strong acid by strong base. The titration graph will have the form shown in Fig. 4.14. Rounding of the graph near the equivalence point is due to water dissociation. This latter is immaterial since it is only necessary

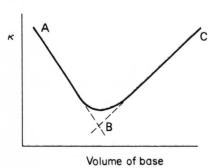

Volume of base

FIGURE 4.14

to take a number of points well to either side of the equivalence point and to extrapolate the two linear segments to the equivalence point. The explanation of the shape of the graph is very simple: over the region AB the fast-moving hydrogen ions of the acid are replaced by the more slowly moving base cations with a consequent fall in conductivity. After all the hydrogen ions are removed, the conductivity rises between B and C as an excess of hydroxyl ions is added to the solution.

(2) Titration of weak acid by strong base. The type of titration graph obtained in this case is shown in Fig. 4.15. The conductivity initially rises from A to B as the salt e.g. sodium acetate is formed. Any contribution to the overall conductivity by that of hydrogen ions is largely suppressed by the buffering action of the acetate ion. Beyond the equivalence point, the conductivity increases from B to C due to the increasing concentration of hydroxyl ions.

(3) Titration of strong acid by weak base. The titration plot will take the

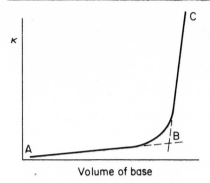

FIGURE 4.15
Shape of conductimetric titration graph for titration of weak acid by strong base.

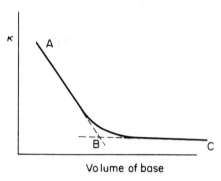

FIGURE 4.16
Shape of conductimetric titration graph for titration of strong acid by weak base.

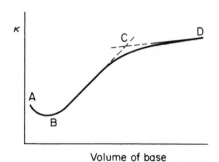

FIGURE 4.17
Shape of conductimetric titration graph for titration of weak acid by weak base.

form shown in Fig. 4.16. An initial rapid decline over the region AB is due to the replacement of the mobile hydrogen ions by cations of the weak base. From B to C the weak base is added in excess to a solution of its salt so that its ionization is suppressed. Consequently, the conductivity of the excess hydroxyl ions is negligible.

(4) Titration of weak acid with weak base. In such cases, titration curves of the type shown in Fig. 4.17 are obtained. Over the region AB, corresponding to the initial addition of weak base, the ionization of the weak acid is suppressed by the buffer action so that the conductivity falls. As the salt is progressively formed, the number of ions in solution rises with consequent increase in conductivity over BC. In the region CD, addition of the weakly ionized base to a solution of its salt causes the conductivity to almost level off.

Further reading

Davies, C. W. (1933), *The Conductivity of Solutions*, 2nd Edn., Chapman and Hall, London.
Gurney, R. W. (1967), *Ionic Processes in Solution*, McGraw-Hill, New York.
MacInnes, D. A. (1947), *The Principles of Electrochemistry*, 2nd Edn., Reinhold, New York.
Robinson, R. A. and Stokes, R. H. (1959), *Electrolyte Solutions*, 2nd Edn., Butterworths, London.

'Reversible' (equilibrium) potentials

5

5.1 Comparison of chemical and electrochemical reactions

Electrode reactions are oxidation–reduction processes of a somewhat unique type which obey the scheme:

$$\text{oxidant} + n\text{e} \rightleftharpoons \text{reductant} \tag{5.1}$$

ne representing a transfer of n unit charges, i.e. electrons.

The difference between chemical and electrochemical reactions lies in the different sources of electrons. A chemical oxidation–reduction system is made up of two individual systems, e.g.

$$\text{Ox}_1 + n\text{e} \rightleftharpoons \text{Red}_1$$
$$\text{Red}_2 - n\text{e} \rightleftharpoons \text{Ox}_2$$

Overall

$$\text{Ox}_1 + \text{Red}_2 \rightleftharpoons \text{Red}_1 + \text{Ox}_2 \tag{5.2}$$

It is not possible to isolate the two contributing processes, since one can only observe changes in one system by coupling it with the second.

Electrochemically, the individual processes may be separated. It is, for instance, often possible for a metallic conductor, dipping into a solution of an oxidizing or reducing agent, to exchange electrons with such species and effectively bring about their reduction or oxidation. Such reactions are in some ways simpler in that if the electrode is only providing or taking up electrons it may otherwise be regarded as inert.

It is possible to control fairly precisely the rate with which electrons are provided (or taken up) by an electrode by variation of a potential applied to it via an externally connected e.m.f. source (the circuit being completed by the inclusion of a suitable reference electrode). This, in turn, makes it possible to control the rates of electrochemical processes with some precision.

We shall be concerned with *two* ways in which such electron-exchange reactions may occur. They may be *forced* to occur (as above), which is the situation encountered in all processes of electrolysis. They may occur *spontaneously* in batteries and galvanic cells.

When two electrochemical redox systems are coupled together, one electrode providing and the other taking up electrons, the *net* effect will be similar to that indicated in the *chemical* scheme. Such is the situation observed with electrochemical cells for which there are associated overall chemical reactions. Further, owing to the precision with which electrochemical measurements may be made for such systems, it is often possible to use them to obtain precise thermodynamic data characteristic of reactions occurring within cells.

5.1.1   Mass transfer and electron-exchange processes

In considering electron-exchange reactions at electrodes we are concerned essentially with the layer of solution very close to the electrode surface. It must be borne in mind, however, that an oxidant or reductant in solution has to have some means of reaching the electrode vicinity. There are a number of ways in which this can occur and these are included under the general heading of mass transfer processes. They are:

(a) *Migration*–the movement of cations and anions through a solution under the influence of an applied potential between electrodes placed in that solution. This phenomenon we have met already, and we have discussed the significance and practical determination of transport numbers.

(b) *Diffusion*–an electrode reaction depletes the concentration of oxidant or reductant at an electrode surface and produces a concentration gradient there. This gives rise to the movement of species from the higher to the lower concentration. Unlike migration, which only occurs for charged particles, diffusion occurs for both charged and uncharged species.

(c) *Convection*–this includes thermal and stirring effects which can arise extraneously through vibration, shock and the setting up of temperature gradients, or through controlled agitation or stirring.

91

Considerable variation in the relative rates of mass transfer and electron-exchange processes is possible. The simplest interpretation of electrochemical reactions assumes that the rates of *all* processes are virtually infinite.

5.2   Reversible electrode potentials

A metal dipping into a solution of its ions has an equilibrium such as

$$M^{n+} + ne \rightleftharpoons M \tag{5.3}$$

eventually established at its surface. For many systems such a situation is established rapidly, in other cases it may be extremely slow. Such an electrode will adopt a potential whose value is a function of the position of equilibrium for reactions (5.3). If this is established rapidly, the potential may be easily measured via a potentiometer device by comparison with another (reference) electrode. If the process is a slow one, a continuously variable potential will be observed and no steady value may be determined experimentally. For a thermodynamic equilibrium, the potential adopted is known as the *reversible electrode potential.*

Other electrodes involve gases in equilibrium with ions in solution, e.g. hydrogen and chlorine electrodes function through operation of the following equilibria

$$\tfrac{1}{2} H_2 \rightleftharpoons H^+ + e \tag{5.4}$$

and

$$\tfrac{1}{2} Cl_2 + e \rightleftharpoons Cl^- \tag{5.5}$$

These require the gas to be bubbled over the surface of some inert electrode material dipping into a solution of the ions of the gas. Surface adsorbed gas molecules then enter into equilibrium with ions in solution and cause the electrode to adopt a potential characteristic of the position of equilibrium. For the hydrogen electrode it is seen that the oxidized form is in solution, while for the chlorine electrode the oxidized form is adsorbed at the surface. In a further type of electrode (redox electrode) both oxidized and reduced forms occur in solution, electrons being donated or accepted by an inert conductor immersed in the solution. An example is provided by the ferrous–ferric system

$$Fe^{3+} + e \rightleftharpoons Fe^{2+} \qquad (5.6)$$

Each of the electrode systems described above constitutes what is known as a 'half-cell' and it is necessary to couple two such half-cells to form a complete electrochemical cell. When all the equilibrium components of a half-cell are in their standard states of unit activity, the electrode is said to be a *Standard Electrode* and to adopt its *Standard Potential.*

5.2.1 *Electrode potentials and activity. The Nernst equation*

The van't Hoff reaction equation expresses the free energy change for a chemical reaction in the form

$$\Delta G = \Delta G^{\ominus} + RT \ln \frac{\Pi \text{ (activities of products)}}{\Pi \text{ (activities of reactants)}} \qquad (5.7)$$

Thus, for the electrode reaction (5.3), Equation (5.7) takes the form

$$\Delta G = \Delta G^{\ominus} + RT \ln \frac{a_M}{a_{M^{n+}}} \qquad (5.8)$$

Now, the free energy change of a reversible electrode reaction is related to the electrode potential by

$$\Delta G = -nEF \qquad (5.9)$$

Or, for the standard state

$$\Delta G^{\ominus} = -nE^{\ominus}F \qquad (5.10)$$

$\Delta G^{\ominus}$ and $E^{\ominus}$ being the standard free energy change and electrode potential respectively. Relations in Equations (5.9) and (5.10) may be derived simply as follows. Reduction of one mole of M^{n+} to M requires the passage of n faradays, or a quantity of electricity nF coulombs. A charge nF is thus passed through a potential difference of E volts, so that the electrical work done is nFE joules. This work done *by* the system, at constant temperature and pressure, is equal to the *decrease* in free energy of the system, $-\Delta G$. Hence the equality in Equation (5.9), and, under standard conditions (5.10).

Substitution of Equations (5.9) and (5.10) into (5.8) gives

$$nEF = nE^{\ominus}F + RT \ln \frac{a_{M^{n+}}}{a_M}$$

or,

$$E = E^{\ominus} + \frac{RT}{nF} \ln a_{M^{n+}} \tag{5.11}$$

where a_M has been omitted as the activity of the metal may be regarded as constant and unity. The logarithmic term always involves a ratio of terms characteristic of the oxidized form to those characteristic of the reduced form. Thus, for a redox electrode, e.g. the ferric–ferrous system

$$E = E^{\ominus} + \frac{RT}{F} \ln \frac{a_{Fe^{3+}}}{a_{Fe^{2+}}} \tag{5.12}$$

and for a chlorine electrode,

$$E = E^{\ominus} + \frac{RT}{F} \ln \frac{a_{Cl_2}^{1/2}}{a_{Cl^-}}$$

$$= E^{\ominus} + \frac{RT}{F} \ln \frac{1}{a_{Cl^-}} \tag{5.13}$$

since $a_{Cl_2}^{1/2} = 1$ at 1 atmosphere pressure.

Thus, in general,

$$E_{eq} = E^{\ominus} + \frac{RT}{nF} \ln \frac{[Ox]}{[Red]} \tag{5.14}$$

This is the Nernst equation, in which E_{eq} has been used to emphasize that it is an equilibrium potential referring to the position of dynamic equilibrium between oxidized and reduced forms which is established rapidly at the electrode surface. Only to such a system can this – a thermodynamic equation – be applied.

The equilibrium at the electrode may be disturbed by making it more oxidizing or reducing by superimposing an external e.m.f. Thus, if a potential, E, is applied such that $E < E_{eq}$, some of the oxidized form is reduced until a new equilibrium position is reached where $E'_{eq} = E$. Conversely, if $E > E_{eq}$, some of the reduced form is oxidized. Such changes may only be made within limits which are consistent with equilibrium being maintained at the electrode. While such an approach may be useful, it is much oversimplified; electron exchanges proceed with finite rates which vary widely and mass transfer processes occur at finite speeds. It is, however, convenient to consider cases where (i) the electron exchange rate > mass transfer rate and (ii) mass transfer rate > electron transfer rate.

5.2.2 'Fast' and 'slow' electrode processes

Consider the reduction of an oxidant at an electrode (cathode). This may be followed in practice by means of a circuit of the type referred to in 5.1, the *net* current flowing being plotted as a function of the applied potential. Such current–voltage curves are of great use in the study of electrode processes.

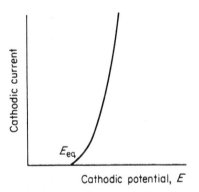

Cathodic potential, E

FIGURE 5.1
Current–potential curve for a cathodic process.

For the moment, let us assume that the electrode material is, in fact, the reduced form of the oxidant, so that if the oxidant is the metal ion M^+, the electrode consists of metal M. If equilibrium between M and M^+ is established instantaneously, M will adopt a characteristic potential with respect to that of the reference electrode (which must remain constant). No net current will be observed since identical currents flow in either direction due to identical movements of charge in both directions. As soon as a potential is applied more

95

negative (more reducing, or more cathodic) than E_{eq} a net current flows since the process

$$M^+ + e \rightarrow M$$

is accelerated relative to the other (Fig. 5.1).

If a potential is applied more positive (more oxidizing, or more anodic) than E_{eq} a net current flows in the opposite direction, since the process

$$M \rightarrow M^+ + e$$

now occurs. The current–voltage graph takes the form shown in Fig. 5.2. Similar considerations apply to oxidation and reduction processes at inert electrodes. Let us consider the same metal ion M^+ and its reduction at such

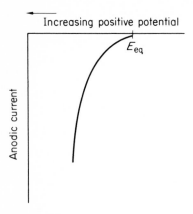

FIGURE 5.2
Current–potential curve for an anodic process.

an inert electrode, i.e. one with which it does not react or enter into equilibrium. In this case no current will be observed until E_{eq} is reached, since only the oxidized form, M^+, is present with none of the reduced form, M. If the reduced form, M, can be dissolved in the electrode, e.g. in the form of an amalgam in the case of a mercury electrode, the corresponding anodic current–voltage curve may be obtained. To do this the amalgam electrode and reference electrode would have to be placed in a solution containing no M^+ but some indifferent electrolyte to act as current carrier. At potentials with respect to the reference electrode more negative than E_{eq} no net current would be observed, but at more positive values a net anodic current would appear (Fig. 5.3).

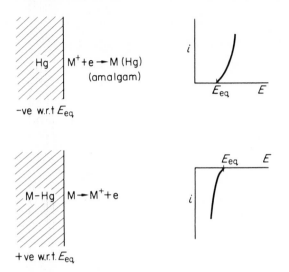

FIGURE 5.3
Cathodic and anodic reactions, with corresponding current–potential curves, at an inert electrode in which the reduced form is soluble.

Consider now a redox system, e.g. M^{3+}/M^{2+}, and let both forms be present in a solution into which are placed an inert electrode and a suitable reference electrode. This inert electrode may be called the 'indicator electrode', since it is the behaviour of the redox couple at this electrode which is being investigated. If the equilibrium

$$M^{3+} + e \rightleftharpoons M^{2+}$$

is established instantaneously at the electrode surface then, with no externally applied potential, the inert electrode adopts a characteristic potential, E_{eq}. At potentials more negative than E_{eq} the current–voltage curve for the process $M^{3+} + e \rightarrow M^{2+}$ may be drawn while at more positive potentials the curve for the process $M^{2+} - e \rightarrow M^{3+}$ occurs, the one passing smoothly into the other via the value E_{eq} (Fig. 5.4). All systems considered so far in this section may be classed as 'fast' or reversible, the term fast referring to the rapid attainment

97

of equilibrium between an electrode and species in solution. Figure 5.4 shows the variation of net current with applied potential (dotted curve) in relation to the currents for the individual forward and backward processes. This shows

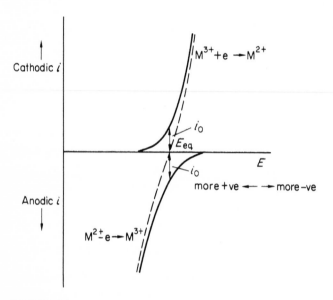

FIGURE 5.4
Anodic–cathodic current-potential curve for a 'fast' system.

more clearly the flow of equal and opposite currents at E_{eq} – these being denoted by i_0, the exchange current. For such a system at potentials only slightly removed from E_{eq}, a net oxidation or reduction process may be made to occur *under almost reversible conditions* – hence the common description 'reversible' for such cases.

In the case of slow or 'irreversible' systems, equilibrium is established so slowly that the condition is not observable. No significant current is seen near to E_{eq} and potentials often well removed to both cathodic and anodic sides of this value are often required to produce currents of the same order as those obtained for a fast system. In Fig. 5.5 are shown schematically the shapes of current-voltage curves to be expected for a slow anodic–cathodic reaction. It is seen that, not only is a considerably more negative potential

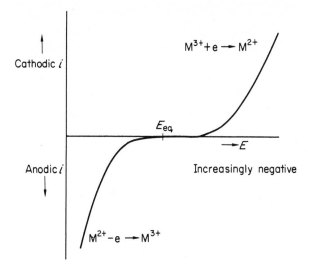

FIGURE 5.5
Anodic–cathodic current potential curve for a 'slow' system.

required for the slow system in order to obtain the same current as for the fast one, but the rate of increase of current is much less for the slow process. For the fast system the current rises almost vertically. In practice this would show some small deviation from the vertical and this reflects the influence of the comparative slowness of mass transfer processes. Slow electrochemical systems are said to require large *overvoltage*, $(E - E_{eq})$ or $(E_{eq} - E)$, in order to produce a significant net current and take place under *irreversible* conditions.

When an electrochemical reaction occurs the concentration of oxidizable or reducible species at the electrode surface is depleted and if fresh material is not provided electrolysis stops. In fact, mass transfer occurs, which tends to maintain surface concentrations constant. If the electrode reaction occurs much more rapidly than mass transfer processes, the latter are rate-determining and control the magnitude of the current which flows. This gives rise finally to a stationary state in which material reaching the electrode is oxidized or reduced as fast as it arrives at the surface.

5.3   The hydrogen scale

In the last section we considered variation of the potential of an electrode with respect to some reference electrode. It is impossible to determine the absolute potentials which electrodes adopt; all that can be done is to measure the e.m.f. of the cell obtained by coupling the electrode in question with another electrode. If, however, this latter maintains an almost constant potential whatever the applied potential difference between the two electrodes, electrode potentials can be measured with respect to an arbitrarily chosen standard and given physical meaning. The standard is the hydrogen electrode which, with hydrogen gas at 1 atmosphere pressure, in contact with platinized platinum in a solution of hydrogen ions of unit activity is assigned a potential of zero *at all temperatures.*

5.3.1   *The standard hydrogen electrode*

The hydrogen electrode, depending on the reversible reaction

$$\tfrac{1}{2} H_2 \rightleftharpoons H^+ + e$$

requires that gaseous hydrogen and hydrogen ions in solution be brought into equilibrium. This condition is attained rapidly at a platinum black surface which functions as a catalyst. The finely divided platinum is supported on platinum foil acting as an electronic conductor. This part of the electrode is made by first cleaning the foil in chromic acid and then plating it in a solution of 1% platinic chloride with an anode of platinum. The necessary thin layer of the catalytic material is in this way cathodically deposited on the foil. Unfortunately, this process causes the occlusion of some chlorine in the deposit and this must be removed by making the electrode the cathode for a short-term electrolysis in dilute sulphuric acid. Chlorine is swept away in the stream of electrolytically generated hydrogen.

   In operation this electrode dips into a solution of hydrogen ions of constant activity while hydrogen gas passes over its surface. In Fig. 5.6 are shown two types of hydrogen electrode: the one has the electrolyte solution enclosed and protected from possible air contamination, the other may be dipped into a solution whose hydrogen ion concentration is to be determined. The former is more desirable for the determination of electrode potentials, the latter is suited for following changes in hydrogen ion concentrations as in titrations.

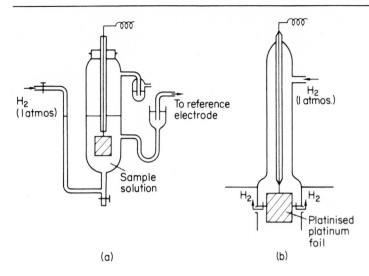

FIGURE 5.6
Two forms of hydrogen electrode.

(a) Lindsey type: hydrogen bubbles upwards over the platinum foil surface.
(b) Hildebrand type: a series of holes are blown in the glass envelope surrounding the platinum foil. The gas flow rate is adjusted so that hydrogen only escapes through these. The level of solution inside the envelope fluctuates so that part of the foil is exposed alternately to solution and gas.

It is vital that the hydrogen gas is pure and for the most accurate work even commercially pure hydrogen should be bubbled through alkaline pyrogallol or passed over heated palladized asbestos to remove the last traces of oxygen. Since the passage of gas through the electrode solution can cause a change of its concentration, prior passage of the purified gas through a sample of this solution is desirable.

Satisfactory functioning of the hydrogen electrode is, above all, dependent on the complete absence of catalyst poisons such as mercury and arsenic and particularly sulphur compounds. Consequently, rubber tubing should not be used for connections unless pre-treated by boiling in concentrated sodium hydroxide solution. P.V.C. or Polythene are much more reliable materials to use. Before using a hydrogen electrode to determine the e.m.f. of a cell formed by coupling it with another half-cell, it should be checked against a duplicate electrode. The steady e.m.f. of a cell made up of two identical

101

hydrogen half-cells should, of course, be zero. In operation a hydrogen electrode should be found to assume a steady potential within 20 minutes and this should be independent of the rate of bubbling. Dependence of the potential on bubbling rate is characteristic of poisoning as are also slowness in reaching equilibrium and general variability of potential. Under these conditions it is necessary to clean and replatinize the electrode surface.

By applying the Nernst equation to the hydrogen electrode equilibrium it is seen that the potential of a hydrogen electrode is given by

$$E = E^{\ominus} + \frac{RT}{F} \ln \frac{a_{H^+}}{a_{H_2}^{1/2}} = E^{\ominus} + \frac{RT}{F} \ln a_{H^+} - \frac{RT}{2F} \ln p_{H_2} \quad (5.15)$$

where p_{H_2} is the pressure of hydrogen gas.

When both the activities of hydrogen and hydrogen ion are unity $E = E^{\ominus}$ which is arbitrarily given the value zero at all temperatures. Potentials of all other electrodes may then be given values relative to this standard.

5.3.2 Electrode potential and cell e.m.f. sign conventions

In the past the question of signs which are to be given to electrode potentials and cell e.m.f.'s has caused great confusion on account of differing conventions. The convention adopted by the International Union of Pure and Applied Chemistry (I.U.P.A.C.) is the one which should be used and which will be used throughout this book.

By the electrode potential of the half-cell M^{n+}/M is implied the e.m.f. of the cell formed by coupling the latter with a hydrogen half-cell. Since the potential of the latter is zero under standard conditions, the e.m.f. determined is the electrode potential of the M^{n+}/M couple. The cell may be represented by

$$\text{Pt, H}_2 \ (a = 1)|\text{H}^+ \ (a = 1)||M^{n+}|M \quad (5.16)$$

the electrode potential of the couple M^{n+}/M then being defined by

$$E_{cell} = E_{right} - E_{left} \quad (5.17)$$

with $E_{left} = 0$ for a standard hydrogen electrode.

The sign of the electrode potential is decided very easily by whether hydrogen gas is evolved or hydrogen ionizes at the left-hand electrode. If on closing the circuit of cell (5.16) the hydrogen becomes the *positive* pole by giving up electrons to hydrogen ions to give gaseous hydrogen, the unknown electrode potential is *negative* and equal to the e.m.f. developed by the cell. On the other hand, if the hydrogen electrode becomes the *negative* pole, taking up electrons as hydrogen ionizes, the unknown electrode potential is *positive* and again equal to the e.m.f. developed by the cell. A table of International Standard Electrode Potentials on the hydrogen scale is given below (Table 5.1).

TABLE 5.1
Standard electrode potentials, $E^{\ominus}$ (volts, w.r.t.S.H.E.), at 298 K

Electrode	$E^{\ominus}$	Electrode	$E^{\ominus}$
Li^+/Li	-3.05	Cu^{2+}/Cu^+	$+0.16$
Ca^{2+}/Ca	-2.87	Bi^{3+}/Bi	$+0.23$
Na^+/Na	-2.71	Cu^{2+}/Cu	$+0.34$
Mg^{2+}/Mg	-2.37	O_2/OH^-	$+0.40$
Al^{3+}/Al	-1.66	Fe^{3+}/Fe^{2+}	$+0.76$
Zn^{2+}/Zn	-0.76	Ag^+/Ag	$+0.80$
Cd^{2+}/Cd	-0.40	Hg^{2+}/Hg	$+0.80$
Ni^{2+}/Ni	-0.25	Hg^{2+}/Hg_2^{2+}	$+0.92$
Pb^{2+}/Pb	-0.13	Cl_2/Cl^-	$+1.36$
H^+/H	0.00	Ce^{4+}/Ce^{3+}	$+1.45$

When an electrochemical cell is formed from two half-cells, one of which is not the hydrogen half-cell, the e.m.f. may be calculated from rule (5.17) using the individual half-cell potentials determined with respect to hydrogen. The electrode which has the more negative potential is *always* written on the *left* as the negative pole of the cell, while that with the more positive electrode potential is *always* written on the *right* as the positive pole of the cell. When this rule is followed, no ambiguity as to signs arises. Consider the Daniell cell in which one electrode is zinc dipping into a zinc sulphate solution, the other being copper dipping into copper sulphate solution. The two solutions are prevented from mixing by a porous membrane separating them. In accordance with the convention this cell may be represented by

$$Zn/ZnSO_4 \quad \vdots \quad CuSO_4/Cu$$

i.e.

$$Zn/Zn^{2+} \quad \vdots \quad Cu^{2+}/Cu \tag{5.18}$$

103

In performing calculations on such cells, it is a useful practice to write down all the information, including electrode reactions, known about the two half-cells to the left and right as follows.

Left-hand electrode	*Right-hand electrode*
Negative pole of cell	Positive pole of cell
Oxidation process occurs	Reduction process occurs
$Zn \rightarrow Zn^{2+} + 2e$	$Cu^{2+} + 2e \rightarrow Cu$
$E^{\ominus} = -0.76$ volt ($v.$ S.H.E.)	$E^{\ominus} = +0.34$ volt ($v.$ S.H.E.)

Overall

$$Zn + Cu^{2+} \rightarrow Zn^{2+} + Cu$$
$$E^{\ominus}_{cell} = +0.34 - (-0.76)$$
$$= +1.10 \text{ volt}$$

It can be seen that when the cell is represented correctly there is no ambiguity as to the direction in which the reaction proceeds.

5.4 Other reference electrodes

It is often more convenient in practice to use subsidiary reference electrodes whose potentials have been accurately determined with respect to the hydrogen electrode. Such electrode systems are carefully chosen to give reproducible potentials over a long period of time. Quite apart from the practical inconvenience of using a hydrogen electrode (which, incidentally, is often much exaggerated), subsidiary reference electrodes can be chosen which do not show the more important disadvantages of the primary standard which cannot be used in solutions containing reducible species and is very susceptible to 'poisoning'.

The commonest type of reference electrode is of the following form: metal/saturated solution of sparingly soluble salt of metal + additional strongly ionized salt with a common anion. The calomel electrode is a case in point, represented by

$$Hg/Hg_2Cl_2 \text{ (s), KCl aq.}$$

Other examples are the silver/silver chloride and mercury/mercurous sulphate electrodes,

$$Ag/AgCl(s), KCl \text{ aq.}$$

and

$$Hg/Hg_2SO_4(s), K_2SO_4 \text{ aq.}$$

The potential adopted by each of these reference electrodes is controlled by the activity of the anion in solution. Thus there are three types of calomel electrode corresponding to 0·1 M, M and saturated KCl whose potentials, on the hydrogen scale, at 298 K are collected in Table 5.2. Two forms of saturated calomel electrode and their components are shown in Fig. 5.7.

TABLE 5.2

Electrode	Potential (volts, v. S.H.E.)
0·1 M KCl calomel	+0·336
M KCl calomel	+0·283
satd. KCl calomel	+0·244

Consider a calomel electrode containing KCl, the activity of the chloride ions in the solution being a_{Cl^-}. The potential of the mercury depends upon the activity of the mercurous ions, Hg_2^{2+}, so that

$$E = E_{Hg}^{\ominus} + \frac{RT}{2F} \ln a_{Hg_2^{2+}} \tag{5.19}$$

Now, $a_{Hg_2^{2+}} \times a_{Cl^-}^{-2} = K_{Hg_2Cl_2}$, the solubility product of calomel, i.e.,

$$a_{Hg_2^{2+}} = \frac{K_{Hg_2Cl_2}}{a_{Cl^-}^{-2}} \tag{5.20}$$

Substitution of Equation (5.20) into Equation (5.19) gives

$$E = E_{Hg}^{\ominus} + \frac{RT}{2F} \ln \frac{K_{Hg_2Cl_2}}{a_{Cl^-}^{-2}} \tag{5.21}$$

105

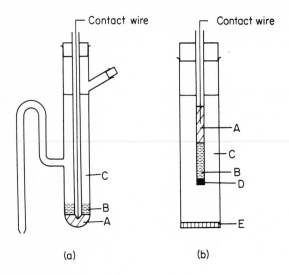

FIGURE 5.7
Two forms of calomel electrode.

A. Mercury.
B. Mercury–calomel paste.
C. Potassium chloride solution.
D. Asbestos or glass wool plug.
E. Sintered glass.

or,

$$E = \left[E_{Hg}^{\ominus} + \frac{RT}{2F} \ln K_{Hg_2Cl_2} \right] - \frac{RT}{2F} \ln a_{Cl^-}^{-2} \qquad (5.22)$$

Since the bracketted terms form a constant, which we may denote by $E_{Hg_2Cl_2}^{\ominus}$, Equation (5.22) may take the form

$$E = E_{Hg_2Cl_2}^{\ominus} - \frac{RT}{F} \ln a_{Cl^-} \qquad (5.23)$$

5.5   Electrochemical concentration cells

We have seen that the coupling of two half-cells produces an electrochemical cell which may be used to produce an e.m.f. In the Daniell cell the two half-cell components are brought into electrical contact by a porous membrane separating the copper sulphate and zinc sulphate solutions. There will inevitably be interdiffusion of zinc and copper ions. Usually the ions from such solutions in contact will diffuse at different rates, leading to a charge separation across the interface which will give rise to a potential difference in this region which ultimately becomes steady. Any measurement of the cell e.m.f. will under these conditions include a contribution from this *diffusion* or *liquid junction* potential. Liquid junction potentials are extremely difficult to reproduce in practice and, even though their magnitudes do not normally exceed 100 mV, it is wisest for them to be eliminated if at all possible. This may be achieved by connecting solutions in two half-cells by means of a *salt bridge* (Fig. 5.8). This is either a glass or flexible tube containing a saturated solution of either potassium chloride or ammonium nitrate. To prevent excessive diffusion, the ends of the tubes are often plugged with porous material, such as filter paper or glass wool, and the electrolytes are frequently set in agar gel. Transport numbers of cation and anion in solutions of potassium chloride and ammonium nitrate are approximately equal and if such species

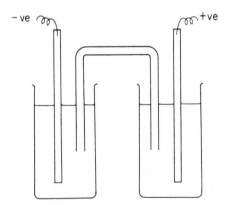

FIGURE 5.8
Connection of half-cells by means of a salt bridge containing a suitable electrolyte to eliminate the junction potential. For KCl and NH_4NO_3, $t_+ \sim t_- \sim 0.5$.

serve to carry current in a salt bridge between two half-cells, the rates of movement of charge in opposite directions will be approximately the same with virtually no charge separation across solution interfaces. In this way liquid junction potentials may be reduced to at most a few millivolts.

Cell e.m.f.'s may be measured potentiometrically by comparison with a standard cell of precisely known and reproducible e.m.f. A Weston Standard Cadmium cell is often used for such purposes and the structure and components of such a cell are shown schematically in Fig. 5.9. A Poggendorf circuit is set up as shown in Fig. 5.10, in which the standard cell and that of unknown

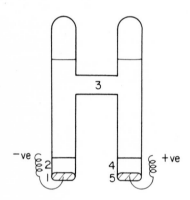

FIGURE 5.9
The Weston Standard Cadmium cell.

1. 12·5% cadmium amalgam.
2. Cadmium sulphate crystals.
3. Saturated cadmium sulphate solution.
4. Mercurous sulphate | cadmium sulphate.
5. Mercury.

e.m.f. are connected in parallel with a switching device so that at any time either one or the other, but not both, are connected in opposition to the bridge potential. The standard cell is first balanced with respect to the potentiometer wire to zero current, i.e. AB $\propto E_{standard}$. A fresh balance is then obtained with the cell under investigation, i.e. AB$'$ $\propto E_{unknown}$, so that

$$E_{unknown} = \frac{AB'}{AB} \cdot E_{standard} \qquad (5.24)$$

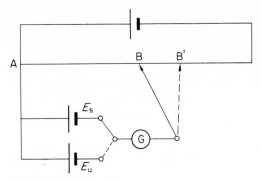

FIGURE 5.10
Poggendorf potentiometric circuit for determination of cell e.m.f.'s.

E_s = e.m.f. of standard
E_u = e.m.f. of unknown
$$\frac{E_u}{E_s} = \frac{AB'}{AB}$$

It is obviously essential that the potentiometer cell and balancing cell should act in opposition. If the polarity of a cell is not known then it must be connected in both possible ways, one of which will give balance, the other will not. The cell polarity is thus determinable in addition to the e.m.f.

5.6   Concentration cells without liquid junctions

Concentration cells are made up of two half-cells which are similar chemically but which differ in the activity of some common component: the difference giving rise to an e.m.f. because of the difference in potential of the two half-cells. This activity difference may be either between the solutions or between the electrode materials.

5.6.1   Cells with amalgam electrodes

Such a cell is formed by two metal amalgam electrodes of different metal activity dipping into a common solution of a soluble salt of the metal, e.g.

$$(-\text{ve pole})\quad \text{Tl}\ \mid\ \text{Hg}\ \mid\ \text{TlNO}_3\ \mid\ \text{Tl}\ \mid\ \text{Hg}\quad (+\text{ve pole})$$

$$a_2 \qquad\qquad\qquad a_1\ (a_2 > a_1)$$

$$E_2 \qquad\qquad\qquad E_1$$

109

activity of Tl^+ ions in solution $= a_+$.

Oxidation	*Reduction*
$Tl \rightarrow Tl^+ + e$	$Tl^+ + e \rightarrow Tl$

$$E_2 = E_{Tl}^{\ominus} + \frac{RT}{F} \ln \frac{a_+}{a_2} \qquad\qquad E_1 = E_{Tl}^{\ominus} + \frac{RT}{F} \ln \frac{a_+}{a_1}$$

since $a_2 > a_1$, $E_1 > E_2$. Therefore,

$$E_{cell} = E_1 - E_2 = \frac{RT}{F} \ln \frac{a_2}{a_1} \qquad\qquad (5.25)$$

It should be noted that Equation (5.25) gives the instantaneous cell e.m.f. which will fall as the ratio a_2/a_1 decreases due to transfer of material. Thus, overall, the cell reaction involves the passage of thallium from the higher to the lower activity. When these activities become equal, the potentials of both electrodes are the same and the cell ceases to operate. For the passage of 1 faraday, the free energy change accompanying the movement of 1 mole of thallium from a_2 to a_1 is

$$\Delta G = -RT \ln \frac{a_2}{a_1}$$

and since

$$\Delta G = -nEF \quad (\text{and } n = 1)$$

$$E_{cell} = \frac{RT}{F} \ln \frac{a_2}{a_1} \qquad (\text{see Equation (5.25)})$$

5.6.2 Cells with gas electrodes operating at different pressures

Here we may consider a cell consisting of two hydrogen electrodes operating at different pressures dipping into a common solution of hydrochloric acid, e.g.

$(-\text{ve pole})$		$(+\text{ve pole})$
Pt, H_2	HCl	H_2, Pt
p_2		$p_1 \ (p_2 > p_1)$
E_2		E_1

Oxidation	*Reduction*
$\frac{1}{2} H_2 \rightarrow H^+ + e$	$H^+ + e \rightarrow \frac{1}{2} H_2$

$$E_2 = E_{H_2}^{\ominus} + \frac{RT}{nF} \ln \frac{a_{H^+}}{a_{H_2}^{1/2}} \qquad E_1 = E_{H_2}^{\ominus} + \frac{RT}{F} \ln \frac{a_{H^+}}{a_{H_2}^{1/2}}$$

$$= \frac{RT}{F} \ln a_{H^+} - \frac{RT}{F} \ln p_2^{1/2} \qquad = \frac{RT}{F} \ln a_{H^+} - \frac{RT}{F} \ln p_1^{1/2}$$

Thus, $E_1 > E_2$. Therefore,

$$E_{cell} = E_1 - E_2 = \frac{RT}{2F} \ln \frac{p_2}{p_1} \qquad (5.26)$$

5.6.3 Concentration cells without transference

One can form such a cell by connecting two cells of the Harned type in opposition to one another; in this way a composite cell is formed.

The simplest type of Harned cell is

$(-$ve pole$)$ $(+$ve pole$)$

H_2 (1 atm), Pt | HCl | AgCl(s), Ag

Oxidation	*Reduction*
$\frac{1}{2} H_2 \rightarrow H^+ + e$	$AgCl(s) + e \rightarrow Ag(s) + Cl^-$

Overall cell reaction:

$$\frac{1}{2} H_2 \text{ (1 atm)} + AgCl(s) \rightarrow Ag(s) + H^+ + Cl^-$$

Thus, the free energy change for the passage of 1 faraday is,

$$\Delta G = -nFE = \Delta G^{\ominus} + RT \ln \frac{a_{Ag} \cdot a_{H^+} \cdot a_{Cl^-}}{a_{H_2}^{1/2} \cdot a_{AgCl}}$$

which, since the activities of silver, hydrogen and silver chloride are constant and unity, becomes

$$\Delta G = \Delta G^{\ominus} + RT \ln a_{H^+} a_{Cl^-}$$

or

$$E = E^{\ominus} - \frac{RT}{F} \ln a_{H^+} a_{Cl^-} = E^{\ominus} - \frac{2RT}{F} \ln (a_{\pm})_{HCl} \qquad (5.27)$$

111

Such cells are useful for determining mean ion activity coefficients of acids in the central solution (see Chapter 6).

A composite of two such cells may be represented by

Ag, AgCl(s) | HCl | Pt, H$_2$ (1 atm) $\quad$ Pt, H$_2$ (1 atm) | HCl | AgCl(s), Ag

$$(a_\pm)_1 \qquad\qquad\qquad\qquad\qquad (a_\pm)_2$$
$$E_1 \qquad\qquad\qquad\qquad\qquad\quad E_2$$

It is seen that the left-hand portion of the composite cell is made to function in the non-spontaneous direction while the right-hand portion is identical with the cell considered above.

It is evident, from Equation (5.27), that if $(a_\pm)_1 > (a_\pm)_2$, $E_2 > E_1$; no physical transfer of material occurs from one side to the other, since no form of liquid junction connects them. The net effect is simply a decline in $(a_\pm)_2$ and an increase in $(a_\pm)_1$ so that the e.m.f. of the cell is given by

$$E = -\frac{\Delta G}{F} = \frac{RT}{F} \ln \frac{(a_{H^+})_2 (a_{Cl^-})_2}{(a_{H^+})_1 (a_{Cl^-})_1}$$

$$E = \frac{2RT}{F} \ln \frac{(a_\pm)_2}{(a_\pm)_1} \tag{5.28}$$

Or, for the general case with an electrolyte comprising ν_+ cations and ν_- anions ($\nu_+ + \nu_- = \nu$) Equation (5.28) becomes

$$E = \frac{\nu}{\nu_\pm} \frac{RT}{F} \ln \frac{(a_\pm)_2}{(a_\pm)_1} \tag{5.29}$$

ν_+ or ν_- being used in the latter expression according to whether the outer electrodes of a cell of this kind are reversible with respect to cations or anions. It is seen that Equation (5.28) is consistent with this general form.

5.7 Concentration cells with liquid junctions

Cells within this category may be conveniently divided into two classes according to whether a *liquid junction potential* is present or eliminated by connection of the two half-cells by means of a salt bridge.

5.7.1 Cells with a liquid junction potential

Consider two half-cells having identical electrodes dipping into their respective solutions containing the same electrolyte but at different mean ion activities. Electrical contact between the half-cells is made by the two solutions meeting at a junction. Such a cell may be represented by

$$M \mid MX \qquad \vdots \qquad MX \mid M$$
$$(a_+)_1, (a_-)_1 \qquad (a_+)_2, (a_-)_2$$

with the electrodes reversible with respect to M^+ cations.

At the right-hand electrode, for the passage of 1 faraday, 1 mole of M^+ ions will be deposited. However, migration of t_+ moles of M^+ across the junction will to some extent make good the loss of M^+ by the deposition process. Similarly, at the left-hand electrode, although 1 mole of M dissolves as M^+ ions, t_+ moles migrate out of the region towards the cathode. This behaviour is summarized below.

(-ve pole)	$(a_+)_1, (a_-)_1$	$(a_+)_2, (a_-)_2$	(+ ve pole)
	$M \longrightarrow M^+ + e$	$M^+ + e \longrightarrow M$	
	t_+ moles migrate *out* $\longrightarrow$	t_+ moles migrate *in* $\longrightarrow$	
	net gain of $(1-t_+)$ moles of $M^+ = t_-$ moles at $(a_+)_1$	*net* loss of $(1-t_+)$ moles of $M^+ = t_-$ moles at $(a_+)_2$	
	$\longleftarrow$ *gain* of t_- moles of X^- at $(a_-)_1$	$\longleftarrow$ *loss* of t_- moles of X^- at $(a_-)_2$	

113

t_+, t_- are the *average* transport numbers for the two activities of the electrolyte involved. It is clear that the overall process involves the transfer of material from the higher to the lower activity, viz.,

$$t_- M^+ + t_- X^- \rightarrow t_- M^+ + t_- X^-$$
$$(a_+)_2 \quad (a_-)_2 \quad (a_+)_1 \quad (a_-)_1$$

For this process the free energy change per faraday is

$$\Delta G = \Delta G^{\ominus} + RT \ln \frac{(a_+)_1^{t_-} \cdot (a_-)_1^{t_-}}{(a_+)_2^{t_-} \cdot (a_-)_2^{t_-}} \tag{5.30}$$

since, by definition

$$a_+ a_- = (a_\pm)^2; \qquad a_+^{t_-} \cdot a_-^{t_-} = (a_\pm)^{2t_-}$$

therefore,

$$\Delta G = \Delta G^{\ominus} + 2t_- RT \ln \frac{(a_\pm)_1}{(a_\pm)_2}$$

therefore,

$$E_{\text{cell}} = 2t_- \frac{RT}{F} \ln \frac{(a_\pm)_2}{(a_\pm)_1} \tag{5.31}$$

It should be stressed that the transport number which appears in the equation for the cell e.m.f. is that of the ionic species with respect to which the electrodes are *not* reversible. For the general case where the electrolyte species provides v ions of which there are v_+ cations and v_- anions, Equation (5.31) takes the forms

$$E = t_- \cdot \frac{v}{v_+} \cdot \frac{RT}{nF} \ln \frac{(a_\pm)_2}{(a_\pm)_1} \tag{5.32}$$

or,

$$E = t_+ \cdot \frac{\nu}{\nu_-} \cdot \frac{RT}{nF} \ln \frac{(a_\pm)_2}{(a_\pm)_1} \tag{5.33}$$

according to whether the electrodes are reversible with respect to cations, Equation (5.32) or anions, Equation (5.33)

5.7.2 Cells with eliminated liquid junction potentials

Consider now the same half-cells as used in the previous section but joined via a salt bridge. This cell is represented by

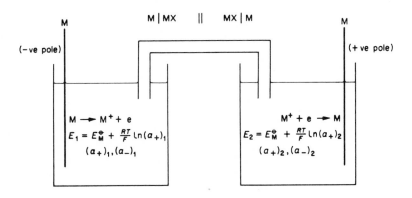

$$E_{cell} = E_2 - E_1 = \frac{RT}{F} \ln \frac{(a_+)_2}{(a_+)_1} \tag{5.34}$$

Now, since individual ion activity coefficients are inaccessible to measurement, the cell e.m.f. must be related to determinable mean ion activities.

By definition,

$$\left(\frac{(a_\pm)_2}{(a_\pm)_1}\right)^2 = \frac{(a_+)_2 (a_-)_2}{(a_+)_1 (a_-)_1}$$

If it is assumed that

$$\frac{(a_+)_2}{(a_+)_1} \sim \frac{(a_-)_2}{(a_-)_1}$$

115

then

$$\frac{(a_\pm)_2}{(a_\pm)_1} \sim \frac{(a_+)_2}{(a_+)_1}$$

and

$$E = \frac{RT}{F} \ln \frac{(a_\pm)_2}{(a_\pm)_1} \qquad (5.35)$$

5.7.3 Calculation of liquid junction potentials

It is apparent that the difference between the e.m.f.'s of the cells considered in sections 5.7.1 and 5.7.2 gives the liquid junction potential involved in the former ($E_{l.j}$). Thus,

$$E_{l.j} = 2t_- \frac{RT}{F} \ln \frac{(a_\pm)_2}{(a_\pm)_1} - \frac{RT}{F} \ln \frac{(a_\pm)_2}{(a_\pm)_1} \qquad (5.36)$$

Therefore,

$$E_{l.j} = (2t_- - 1)\frac{RT}{F} \ln \frac{(a_\pm)_2}{(a_\pm)_1} \qquad (5.37)$$

Now

$$t_+ + t_- = 1$$

Therefore,

$$(2t_- - 1) = t_- - t_+$$

Therefore,

$$E_{l.j} = (t_+ - t_-) . \frac{RT}{F} \ln \frac{(a_\pm)_2}{(a_\pm)_1} \qquad (5.38)$$

This last equation makes clear the function of a salt bridge when eliminating a liquid junction potential. If the electrolyte is chosen such that $t_- = t_+$ then $E_{l.j} = 0$. The general form of Equation (5.37) is

$$E_{l.j} = \left(t_\mp . \frac{\nu}{\nu_\pm} - 1\right)\frac{RT}{nF} \ln \frac{(a_\pm)_2}{(a_\pm)_1} \qquad (5.39)$$

5.7.4 Membrane potentials

When two solutions of the same salt at different concentrations are separated

116

by a membrane which is permeable to both ion species, the potential across the membrane is identifiable with the junction potential between the solutions given by Equation (5.39). If the membrane should have such a pore size that it shows restricted permeability to one ion species, the transport number appearing in Equation (5.39) is then that of this species across the membrane.

Such phenomena are of great significance in biological cell membrane systems. Cell solutions usually contain a higher proportion of potassium salts than sodium salts while external solutions usually show the reverse. The cell surface may therefore be treated as a membrane separating solutions of potassium and sodium ions and which exhibits considerably lower permeability to sodium than to potassium ions. Potassium ions may therefore pass through the membrane from inside to outside the cell at a faster rate than sodium ions pass into the cell. The greater tendency for small, positively charged ions to pass to the outside of the cell leads to a charge distribution in which the interior tends to be negatively charged with respect to the exterior. Although a somewhat crude description, it does in fact summarize the essential condition at the membrane in nerve and muscle cells where electrical impulses are passed from one cell to another.

It is found that the above polarity may be reversed upon addition of species which may disturb the structure of the membrane and open it for transmission of larger ions. Such is the case if a quaternary ammonium salt is introduced near the membrane surface. It would appear that the organic cations are able to penetrate the membrane faster than the inorganic ions, so that they (temporarily at least) open the membrane structure and allow freer passage of inorganic ions. Such a mechanism has been postulated as a contributory factor in the control of the transmission of electrical impulses from one nerve cell to another and from nerve to muscle cells in an organism.

Further reading

Ives, D. J. G. and Janz, G. J. (1961), *Reference Electrodes*, Academic Press, New York and London.
MacInnes, D. A. (1947), *The Principles of Electrochemistry*, 2nd Edn., Reinhold, New York.

Applications of electrode potentials and cell e.m.f's

6

6.1 Thermodynamics of cell reactions

Measurement of the e.m.f. of a reversibly operating cell as well as its temperature coefficient enable ΔG, ΔH and ΔS for the cell reaction to be determined. ΔG at a given temperature follows directly from the cell e.m.f., E by application of the equation

$$\Delta G = -nFE \qquad (6.1)$$

ΔH may be expressed in terms of ΔG in the form of the Gibbs–Helmholtz equation

$$\Delta H = \Delta G - T\left[\frac{\partial(\Delta G)}{\partial T}\right]_P \qquad (6.2)$$

which, in terms of the cell e.m.f., takes the form

$$\Delta H = -nFE - T\left[\frac{\partial(-nFE)}{\partial T}\right]_P \qquad (6.3)$$

or,

$$\Delta H = -nFE + nFT\left(\frac{\partial E}{\partial T}\right)_P \qquad (6.4)$$

$(\partial E/\partial T)_P$ being the temperature coefficient of the cell e.m.f. at constant pressure. In practice this has to be determined very carefully by determining E for the cell over a wide range of temperature so that the tangent to the $E - T$ plot at a given temperature may be drawn and its slope measured.

Once ΔG and ΔH have been found, ΔS may be calculated from

$$\Delta G = \Delta H - T\Delta S \qquad (6.5)$$

119

or

$$\Delta S = \frac{(\Delta H - \Delta G)}{T}$$

therefore,

$$\Delta S = nF \left(\frac{\partial E}{\partial T}\right)_P \qquad (6.6)$$

Since cell e.m.f.'s are measured in volts, the units of ΔH and ΔG are joules and those of ΔS, joules deg^{-1}. Positive, negative and almost zero temperature coefficients have been observed, although negative coefficients are the most usual, signifying that for most cells the electrical energy obtainable from them is less than ΔH because some heat is produced as the cell operates. For positive coefficients the energy obtainable is greater than ΔH and in this case heat must be absorbed from the surroundings when the cell operates and unless a supply of heat is maintained the temperature of such a cell will fall. For a cell with a near zero temperature coefficient the electrical energy is almost identical with the enthalpy change and this is found, for example, with the Daniell Cell. It was somewhat unfortunate that early work with a Daniell cell appeared to confirm the erroneous belief that the electrical energy of a reversible cell was always equal to $-\Delta H$ of the cell reaction.

In principle, electrochemical measurements provide a most sophisticated means of determining such data particularly in the light of the precision with which potentials may be measured when due experimental precautions are taken. It is essential, however, that the reaction under study *does* actually occur in the cell to the exclusion of all others. It is also vital, of course, that *both* the electrodes used in the cell behave reversibly.

6.2 Determination of standard potentials and mean ion activity coefficients

Of particular use in such determinations are cells of the Harned type of which the simplest is represented by

$$\text{H}_2 \text{ (1 atm.), Pt } | \text{ HCl } | \text{ AgCl(s), Ag}$$
$$m$$

m being the molality of the hydrochloric acid. Since the overall cell reaction is

$$\tfrac{1}{2} H_2 + AgCl(s) \rightarrow Ag + H^+ + Cl^- \tag{6.7}$$

$$-\Delta G = nFE = RT \ln K - RT \ln \frac{a_{Ag} \cdot a_{H^+} \cdot a_{Cl^-}}{a_{H_2}^{1/2} \cdot a_{AgCl}} \tag{6.8}$$
$$(n = 1)$$

or,

$$E = E^\ominus - \frac{RT}{F} \ln a_{H^+}a_{Cl^-} = E^\ominus - \frac{2RT}{F} \ln a_\pm \tag{6.9}$$

In terms of the molality of the hydrochloric acid Equation (6.9) becomes

$$E = E^\ominus - \frac{2RT}{F} \ln m - \frac{2RT}{F} \ln \gamma_\pm \tag{6.10}$$

$\gamma_\pm$ being the mean ion activity coefficient of the acid. Equation (6.10) may more usefully be expressed in the form

$$\left(E + \frac{2RT}{F} \ln m\right) = E^\ominus - \frac{2RT}{F} \ln \gamma_\pm \tag{6.11}$$

It is seen that this equation provides a valuable route to the determination of $\gamma_\pm$ but that in order to do this it is necessary to know $E^\ominus$. If a number of measurements of E are made for a range of values of m extending into the region where the Debye–Hückel limiting law holds, i.e. where $\ln \gamma_\pm \propto m^{1/2}$, $E^\ominus$ may be obtained by plotting the left hand side of Equation (6.11) versus $m^{1/2}$. As $m \rightarrow 0$, $\gamma_\pm \rightarrow 1$ so that extrapolation of the line to $m^{1/2} = 0$ gives $E^\ominus$ as intercept.

It is normally better, however, to use forms of the Hückel equation, e.g.

$$-\ln \gamma_\pm = A \left(\frac{\sqrt{m}}{1 + \sqrt{m}} - Bm\right) \tag{6.12}$$

so that

$$\left[E + \frac{2RT}{F} \ln m - \frac{A\sqrt{m}}{1 + \sqrt{m}}\right] = E^\ominus - ABm \tag{6.13}$$

A graph of the left-hand side of Equation (6.13) versus m may be extrapolated to the condition $m = 0$ to give an intercept of $E^\ominus$.

121

Once $E^{\ominus}$ is known, Equation (6.11) may be used to calculate $\gamma_{\pm}$ for any molality of acid. The general principle of the technique may be extended to other electrolytes provided that the cell can be devised so that each electrode is reversible with respect to one of the ions.

Another possibility is to combine two cells of the above type back-to-back in the form of a cell without transference. The e.m.f. of such a cell is given by

$$E = \frac{2RT}{F} \ln \frac{m_2 (\gamma_{\pm})_2}{m_1 (\gamma_{\pm})_1} \tag{6.14}$$

If $(\gamma_{\pm})_1$ is known at molality m_1, $(\gamma_{\pm})_2$ at molality m_2 (or any other molality) may be determined by using Equation (6.14) in the form

$$\frac{EF}{2 \times 2 \cdot 303RT} = \log \frac{m_2}{m_1} + \log \frac{(\gamma_{\pm})_2}{(\gamma_{\pm})_1} \tag{6.15}$$

or,

$$\log (\gamma_{\pm})_2 = \frac{EF}{4 \cdot 606RT} + \log (\gamma_{\pm})_1 - \log \frac{m_2}{m_1} \tag{6.16}$$

$(\gamma_{\pm})_1$ may be determined by the Debye–Hückel relation in *dilute* solution, i.e.,

$$-\log \gamma_{\pm} = \frac{A\sqrt{m}}{1 + \beta a\sqrt{m}} \tag{6.17}$$

(for a 1 : 1 electrolyte). Rearrangement and expansion of Equation (6.17) gives

$$-\log \gamma_{\pm} = A\sqrt{m}(1 + \beta a\sqrt{m})^{-1}$$
$$= A\sqrt{m}(1 - \beta a\sqrt{m} + \cdots)$$
$$= A\sqrt{m} - A\beta a m \tag{6.18}$$

It was shown by Hitchcock that $\log \gamma_{\pm}$ may also be given by

$$\log \gamma_{\pm} = B - \log \frac{(\gamma_{\pm})_1}{(\gamma_{\pm})_2} \tag{6.19}$$

where B is a further constant. Combining Equation (6.19) with Equation (6.18) gives

$$\log \frac{(\gamma_{\pm})_1}{(\gamma_{\pm})_2} - A\sqrt{m} = B(A\beta a)m \tag{6.20}$$

If the left-hand side of Equation (6.20) is plotted against m, a linear plot is obtained of slope $(A\beta a)$ and intercept B. When B is known, the value of log $\gamma_{\pm}$ at any molality may be calculated by means of Equation (6.19).

If transport numbers for electrolyte ions are known reliably over the concentration range used in a cell, it is possible to determine $\gamma_{\pm}$ values from cells with transference. This, however, is a less usual practice.

Amalgam electrodes have proved useful in the determination of values for alkali chlorides and hydroxides using cells such as

$$M(Hg) \mid MCl \mid AgCl(s), Ag$$

or

$$H_2, Pt \mid MOH \mid M(Hg)$$

6.3 Transport number determinations

Comparison of the expressions for the e.m.f.'s of cells with and without transport, for example for the cells

$$Zn \mid ZnSO_4 \quad \vdots \quad ZnSO_4 \mid Zn$$
$$(a_{\pm})_1 \qquad (a_{\pm})_2 \qquad \text{e.m.f. } E_1$$

and

$$Zn \mid ZnSO_4, Hg_2SO_4 \mid Hg \mid Hg_2SO_4, ZnSO_4 \mid Zn \quad \text{e.m.f. } E_2$$
$$(a_{\pm})_1 \qquad\qquad\qquad (a_{\pm})_2$$

shows that the first involves the transport number, t_-, of the sulphate anion, whilst the second does not; thus

$$E_1 = t_- \frac{RT}{F} \ln \frac{(a_{\pm})_2}{(a_{\pm})_1} \qquad (6.21)$$

and

$$E_2 = \frac{RT}{F} \ln \frac{(a_{\pm})_2}{(a_{\pm})_1} \qquad (6.22)$$

123

and

$$\frac{E_1}{E_2} = t_-$$ (6.23)

It must be borne in mind that t_- represents the *average* value of the transport number for the two solutions of mean ion activities $(a_\pm)_1$ and $(a_\pm)_2$. The values of these latter quantities should therefore in practice be as close to one another as is compatible with sufficiently large e.m.f.'s to be precisely measured.

6.4   Determination of equilibrium constants

6.4.1   *Dissociation constants of weak acids*

Such constants may be determined approximately by application of the Henderson–Hasselbalch equation (see Equation (3.40)), viz.

$$pH \sim pK_a + \log\frac{a}{a - b}$$ (6.24)

Where a is the number of moles of a weak monobasic acid in solution and b the number of moles of a strong base added to it so that some of the acid is converted to the salt of the base. It is clear that if $b = a/2$ then $pH = pK_a$. So that, if half the equivalent amount of strong base is added to the weak acid, the pH of the resulting solution is approximately the pK_a value.

More accurate determinations are based upon e.m.f. measurements of Harned-type cells in which the central compartment is occupied by the weak acid, a salt of the acid with a strong base and a strong electrolyte having its cation derived from the strong base and its anion common with that of the electrode anion, e.g.

Pt, H_2 (1 atm.) | HA(m_1), NaA(m_2), NaCl(m_3), AgCl(s) | Ag

The e.m.f. of this cell is given by

$$E_{cell} = E_{AgCl} - E_{H_2}$$ (6.25)

therefore,

$$E_{cell} = E_{AgCl}^{\ominus} - \frac{RT}{F} \ln a_{Cl^-} - \frac{RT}{F} \ln a_{H^+}$$ (6.26)

or,

$$E_{cell} = E_{AgCl}^{\ominus} - \frac{RT}{F} \ln a_{H^+} a_{Cl^-} \tag{6.27}$$

therefore,

$$\frac{F(E_{cell} - E_{AgCl}^{\ominus})}{RT} = -\ln m_{H^+} m_{Cl^-} - \ln \gamma_{H^+} \gamma_{Cl^-} \tag{6.28}$$

Now

$$K_a = \frac{m_{H^+} m_{A^-}}{m_{HA}} \cdot \frac{\gamma_{H^+} \gamma_{A^-}}{\gamma_{HA}}$$

Therefore,

$$\ln K_a = \ln \frac{m_{H^+} m_{A^-}}{m_{HA}} + \ln \frac{\gamma_{H^+} \gamma_{A^-}}{\gamma_{HA}} \tag{6.29}$$

If the right-hand side of Equation (6.29) is added to the right-hand side of Equation (6.28) while the left-hand side of Equation (6.29) is subtracted from it, the equality in Equation (6.28) is in no way affected, thus

$$\frac{F(E_{cell} - E_{AgCl}^{\ominus})}{RT} = -\ln \frac{m_{HA} m_{Cl^-}}{m_{A^-}} - \ln \frac{\gamma_{HA} \gamma_{Cl^-}}{\gamma_{A^-}} - \ln K_a$$

or

$$\left[\frac{F(E_{cell} - E_{AgCl}^{\ominus})}{2 \cdot 303RT} + \log \frac{m_{HA} m_{Cl^-}}{m_{A^-}} \right] = -\log \frac{\gamma_{HA} \gamma_{Cl^-}}{\gamma_{A^-}} - \log K_a \tag{6.30}$$

The e.m.f. of the cell is measured at various values of m_1, m_2 and m_3 and the left-hand side of Equation (6.30) plotted as a function of the ionic strength of the solution. At the condition $I \to 0$, $\gamma'_s \to 1$ and the right-hand side of the equation becomes $-\log K_a$.

Since the sodium chloride is completely dissociated, $m_{Cl^-} = m_3$. HA is partly dissociated into H_3O^+ and A^- so that $m_{HA} = m_1 - m_{H_3O^+} \sim m_1$ if

125

$m_{H_3O^+}$ is small. Also, the A^- ions originate partly from NaA and partly from HA so that $m_{A^-} = m_2 + m_{H_3O^+} \sim m_2$ if $m_{H_3O^+}$ is small.

Thus Equation (6.30) may be reasonably approximated to

$$\left[\frac{F(E_{cell} - E_{AgCl}^{\ominus})}{2 \cdot 303 \, RT} + \log \left(\frac{m_1 m_3}{m_2} \right) \right] = -\log \frac{\gamma_{HA} \gamma_{Cl^-}}{\gamma_{A^-}} - \log K_a \tag{6.31}$$

Figure 6.1 shows the appropriate plot for the system

Pt, H_2 | butyric acid (m_1), sodium butyrate (m_2), NaCl (m_3), AgCl(s) | Ag

Use of Equation (6.31) is restricted to acids with pK_a values in the region of 4 to 5; $m_{H_3O^+}$ must be calculated in the case of stronger acids and the effects of hydrolysis must be taken into account for weaker acids. The important feature of the method is that it is independent of pH measurements. pK_a values determined in this way may be used to standardize the practical pH scale which will be discussed in section 6.5.

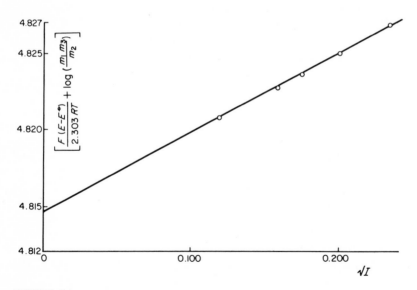

FIGURE 6.1
Determination of the dissociation constant of n-butyric acid in aqueous solution according to Equation (6.31). $-\log_{10} K_a = 4 \cdot 8147$; $K_a = 1 \cdot 52 \times 10^{-5}$.

A further method involves forming a half-cell by immersing a hydrogen electrode in the solution of the acid whose dissociation constant is required. A complete cell is made by coupling this half-cell with a suitable reference electrode via a salt bridge. The acid is titrated with a strong base, the pH of the solution being measured potentiometrically after each addition of base. It is necessary to calibrate the reference electrode and salt bridge with standard buffers if agreement is to be obtained between values of dissociation constants obtained by this method and those resulting from Harned cell measurements, which are independent of pH.

We require a formal expression for $a_{H_3O^+}$ which is provided by the equation for the thermodynamic dissociation constant of the acid, viz.

$$a_{H_3O^+} = \frac{K_a \cdot a_{HA}}{a_{A^-}}$$

$$= K_a \cdot \frac{m_{HA}}{m_{A^-}} \cdot \frac{\gamma_{HA}}{\gamma_{A^-}} \tag{6.32}$$

Let the overall concentration of the acid be m_a; during the course of the titration m_{HA} will decrease as A^- is formed and m_{A^-} increases. At all stages, however,

$$m_a = m_{HA} + m_{A^-} \tag{6.33}$$

If m_b represents the varying concentration of base added during the titration, it is seen that

$$m_b + m_{H^+} = m_{A^-} + m_{OH^-}$$

i.e.

$$m_b = m_{A^-} + m_{OH^-} - m_{H^+} \tag{6.34}$$

Substitution of Equations (6.34) and (6.33) into Equation (6.32) gives

$$a_{H_3O^+} = K_a \left[\frac{m_a - m_{A^-}}{m_b - m_{OH^-} + m_{H^+}} \right] \cdot \frac{\gamma_{HA}}{\gamma_{A^-}}$$

$$= K_a \left[\frac{m_a - m_b + m_{OH^-} - m_{H^+}}{m_b - m_{OH^-} + m_{H^+}} \right] \cdot \frac{\gamma_{HA}}{\gamma_{A^-}}$$

$$= K_a \cdot \frac{m_a - B}{B} \cdot \frac{\gamma_{HA}}{\gamma_{A^-}} \tag{6.35}$$

(where $B = m_b - m_{OH^-} + m_{H^+}$) or,

$$pH = pK_a + \log \frac{B}{m_a - B} + \log \frac{\gamma_{A^-}}{\gamma_{HA}} \tag{6.36}$$

The last term on the right-hand side of Equation (6.36) may be expressed in terms of the Debye–Hückel theory i.e.,

$$\log \frac{\gamma_{A^-}}{\gamma_{HA}} = -A\sqrt{I} + bI \tag{6.37}$$

so that Equation (6.36) becomes

$$A\sqrt{I} - \log \frac{B}{m_a - B} + pH = pK_a + bI \tag{6.38}$$

pK_a may now be determined by plotting the left-hand side of Equation (6.38), for each point of the titration curve, against ionic strength. The value is obtained, by extrapolation to zero ionic strength, as the intercept on the ordinate axis. Calculation of B is facilitated by the application of similar approximations to those used in the Harned method.

In order for the values of pK_a to be in agreement with those obtained by the Harned method, it is vital that the potential of the reference electrode/salt bridge combination is given such a value that the pH values determined during the titration agree with those obtained by calculation from true dissociation constants given by the Harned method.

6.4.2 The ionization constant of water

Again, a cell without a liquid junction is used, e.g.

$$Pt, H_2 \mid MOH(m_1), MCl(m_2) \mid AgCl(s), Ag$$

for which

$$E = E^{\ominus} - \frac{RT}{F} \ln m_{H^+} m_{Cl^-} \gamma_{H^+} \gamma_{Cl^-} \tag{6.39}$$

Now

$$K_W = \frac{a_{H^+} a_{OH^-}}{a_{H_2O}}$$

$$= \frac{\gamma_{H^+} \gamma_{OH^-} m_{H^+} m_{OH^-}}{a_{H_2O}} \tag{6.40}$$

Combining Equations (6.39) and (6.40) we obtain

$$E = E^{\ominus} - \frac{RT}{F} \ln \frac{m_{Cl^-} \gamma_{Cl^-} K_W}{m_{OH^-} \gamma_{OH^-}}$$

$$= E^{\ominus} - \frac{RT}{F} \ln K_W - \frac{RT}{F} \ln \frac{m_{Cl^-}}{m_{OH^-}} - \frac{RT}{F} \ln \frac{\gamma_{Cl^-}}{\gamma_{OH^-}} \quad (6.41)$$

or,

$$\left[E - E^{\ominus} + \frac{RT}{F} \ln \frac{m_2}{m_1} \right] = -\frac{RT}{F} \ln K_W - \frac{RT}{F} \ln \frac{\gamma_{Cl^-}}{\gamma_{OH^-}} \quad (6.42)$$

As before, the left-hand side of Equation (6.42) is plotted as a function of ionic strength (or $\sqrt{}$(ionic strength), which gives a rather better plot) and $-\ln K_w$ determined as the intercept at $I = 0$ when $\gamma_{Cl^-}/\gamma_{OH^-} = 1$.

6.4.3 Solubility products

The problem with such determinations is to devise suitable electrodes and cells. One method is to use the sparingly soluble material as part of an electrode, e.g., to determine K_{AgCl} one could employ a silver–silver chloride electrode. K_{AgCl} may then be measured approximately by coupling the electrode with a reference electrode and determining its potential.

The potential of the silver electrode is given by

$$E = E_{Ag}^{\ominus} + \frac{RT}{F} \ln a_{Ag^+} \quad (6.43)$$

therefore,

$$E = E_{Ag}^{\ominus} + \frac{RT}{F} \ln K_{AgCl} - \frac{RT}{F} \ln a_{Cl^-} \quad (6.44)$$

and since

$$a_{Ag^+} = \frac{K_{AgCl}}{a_{Cl^-}}$$

$$\ln K_{AgCl} = (E - E_{Ag}^{\ominus}) \frac{F}{RT} + \ln a_{Cl^-} \quad (6.45)$$

In order for Equation (6.45) to be used it is required to know $E_{Ag}^{\ominus}$ and a_{Cl^-}; the former must be determined, the latter assumed approximately equal to $a_{\pm}$

of KCl. Since suitable electrode systems can usually be devised, the method is used widely even though it is not particularly accurate.

An alternative method can present serious problems in that it is not always easy to devise a suitable cell. For the determination of K_{AgCl} the following cell could be used

$$Ag \mid AgCl(s), HCl \mid Cl_2, Pt$$
$$1 \text{ atm.}$$

This cell has also the further disadvantages that chlorine electrodes are difficult to use since chlorine attacks platinum while formation of HCl and HClO can alter the composition of the solution. The e.m.f. of the cell is given by

$$E = E_{Cl_2} - E_{Ag}$$

therefore,

$$E = E_{Cl_2}^{\ominus} - \frac{RT}{F} \ln a_{Cl^-} - E_{Ag}^{\ominus} - \frac{RT}{F} \ln K_{AgCl} + \frac{RT}{F} \ln a_{Cl^-}$$
$$(6.46)$$

therefore,

$$E = (E_{Cl_2}^{\ominus} - E_{Ag}^{\ominus}) - \frac{RT}{F} \ln K_{AgCl} \qquad (6.47)$$

From which K_{AgCl} may be found when the standard potential of the silver and chlorine electrode are known.

6.4.4 Equilibrium constants of redox reactions

Standard redox potentials may be used to determine whether reactions proceed quantitatively and whether, therefore, they may be usefully employed analytically. It is well known, for example, that ceric ions oxidize ferrous ions and that this reaction is used for the titrimetric determination of ferrous iron. The usefulness of such reactions may be assessed by considering the redox potentials for the individual redox systems. Thus, we have

$$E_{Fe^{3+}/Fe^{2+}} = E_{Fe^{3+}/Fe^{2+}}^{\ominus} + \frac{RT}{F} \ln \frac{a_{Fe^{3+}}}{a_{Fe^{2+}}}$$
$$(= +0.77 \text{ volt})$$

and

$$E_{Ce^{4+}/Ce^{3+}} = E^{\ominus}_{Ce^{4+}/Ce^{3+}} + \frac{RT}{F} \ln \frac{a_{Ce^{4+}}}{a_{Ce^{3+}}}$$
$$(= +1\cdot61 \text{ volt})$$

The reaction for the cell obtained by combining the two electrodes is

$$Ce^{4+} + Fe^{2+} \rightarrow Fe^{3+} + Ce^{3+} \tag{6.48}$$

If two such half-cells are coupled, the activity of ferric ions increases while that of ferrous ions decreases, causing an *increase* of the ratio $a_{Fe^{3+}}/a_{Fe^{2+}}$. At the same time a decrease in $a_{Ce^{4+}}$ and an increase in $a_{Ce^{3+}}$ leads to a *decrease* in the ratio $a_{Ce^{4+}}/a_{Ce^{3+}}$. Thus, it is seen that the potentials approach each other and meet at the condition of equilibrium when we may write

$$E^{\ominus}_{Fe^{3+}/Fe^{2+}} + \frac{RT}{F} \ln \frac{a_{Fe^{3+}}}{a_{Fe^{2+}}} = E^{\ominus}_{Ce^{4+}/Ce^{3+}} + \frac{RT}{F} \ln \frac{a_{Ce^{4+}}}{a_{Ce^{3+}}} \tag{6.49}$$

therefore,

$$E^{\ominus}_{Ce^{4+}/Ce^{3+}} - E^{\ominus}_{Fe^{3+}/Fe^{2+}} = \frac{RT}{F} \ln \frac{a_{Fe^{3+}}}{a_{Fe^{2+}}} - \frac{RT}{F} \ln \frac{a_{Ce^{4+}}}{a_{Ce^{3+}}} \tag{6.50}$$

$$= \frac{RT}{F} \ln \frac{a_{Fe^{3+}} a_{Ce^{3+}}}{a_{Fe^{2+}} a_{Ce^{4+}}} \tag{6.51}$$

therefore,

$$1\cdot61 - 0\cdot77 = \frac{RT}{F} \ln K$$

K being the equilibrium constant for the redox process. For this case K is seen to be large so that the reaction is quantitatively useful.

6.5 The determination of pH

6.5.1 The hydrogen electrode

From a consideration of the formal definition of pH viz.

$$pH = -\log a_{H^+}$$

it is clear that an electrode in equilibrium with a solution containing hydrogen ions will adopt a potential which is a function of the concentration of hydrogen ions and therefore of the pH of the solution. Since the equilibrium at the electrode is

$$H^+ + e \rightleftharpoons \tfrac{1}{2} H_2$$

the potential adopted is given by

$$E = E^\ominus + \frac{RT}{F} \ln \frac{a_{H^+}}{a_{H_2}^{1/2}}$$

or,

$$E = \frac{RT}{F} \ln a_{H^+} - \frac{RT}{2F} \ln p_{H_2}$$

since $E^\ominus = 0$ by definition for this electrode as the primary standard. Further, if the partial pressure of hydrogen is 1 atmosphere,

$$E = \frac{RT}{F} \ln a_{H^+} \tag{6.52}$$

Exact potentiometric determination of pH using the hydrogen electrode is not as easy as it might at first appear. In principle it could be coupled with a suitable reference electrode to form the cell

$$\text{reference electrode} \parallel H_3O^+ \mid H_2 \mid Pt$$

for which the e.m.f. may be written

$$E = E_{H/H_3O^+} - E_{ref} = \frac{2 \cdot 303 RT}{F} \log a_{H_3O^+} - E_{ref} \tag{6.53}$$

assuming that the liquid junction potential is eliminated. Or, in terms of pH,

$$pH = -\frac{(E + E_{ref})F}{2 \cdot 303 RT} \tag{6.54}$$

However, even if the liquid junction potential is eliminated it is required to know E_{ref}, since the value of pH obtained will be strongly influenced by its value. The value of E_{ref} is calculated assuming that ionic activity coefficients are determined only by the total ionic strength and not by the individual chemical properties of the species.

All that one can hope to do by such a method is to determine pH values which are consistent with those calculated from thermodynamic constants using Equation (6.38). Thus, it is necessary to reassess the values of potential adopted by reference electrodes used for this purpose and also to take appropriate account of liquid junction potentials.

If the pH value determined by using Equation (6.54) is to identify with that used in Equation (6.38), to give the thermodynamic dissociation constant of an acid, then the following equality is necessary

$$-\frac{(E + E_{ref})F}{2 \cdot 303RT} = pK_a + \log\frac{B}{m_a - B} - A\sqrt{I} + bI \qquad (6.55)$$

or,

$$E + \frac{2 \cdot 303RT}{F}\left(pK_a + \log\frac{B}{m_a - B} - A\sqrt{I}\right) = -E_{ref} - \frac{2 \cdot 303RT}{F}bI \qquad (6.56)$$

Experimentally, the hydrogen electrode is immersed in a series of solutions containing weak acids and their salts, the true dissociation constants of the acids being known. Connection of the chosen reference electrode to this solution is achieved by means of a saturated potassium chloride salt bridge. When the left-hand side of Equation (6.56) is plotted as a function of ionic strength, a reassessed value of E_{ref} is obtained as intercept on the I axis. No account has been taken of the liquid junction potential which exists between the salt bridge and the electrolyte solution and whose value varies with both the nature of the buffer used and its concentration. Such variations only produce uncertainties of the order of tenths of millivolts in the value of E_{ref} obtained and the scale of pH values thus obtained constitutes the *conventional* pH scale.

In practice, the use of the hydrogen electrode for pH determinations is severely limited in that it may not be used in solutions containing reducible materials and is easily poisoned by catalytic poisons.

6.5.2 The quinhydrone electrode

This electrode system is now little used as a means of pH determination but it is a good example of an organic redox system which behaves reversibly. For this reason we shall consider its mode of operation.

Quinhydrone is in fact the name given to the molecular crystal formed between quinone and hydroquinone. When dissolved in water the crystal decomposes into its constituent compounds. The redox reaction upon which the electrode operates is

$$\text{O} \quad (Q_{ox}) \qquad + 2\,H^+ + 2\,e \; \rightleftharpoons \qquad \text{OH} \quad (Q_{red}^{2-}) \tag{6.57}$$

although this may be divided into the electrochemical reaction proper and reactions with the solvent.

Thus, in expanded form

$$Q_{ox} + 2\,e \rightleftharpoons Q_{red}^{2-} \tag{6.58a}$$

$$H_2Q_{red} \rightleftharpoons HQ_{red}^- + H^+; \qquad K_1 = \frac{[H^+]\,[HQ_{red}^-]}{[H_2Q_{red}]} \tag{6.58b}$$

$$HQ_{red}^- \rightleftharpoons Q_{red}^{2-} + H^+; \qquad K_2 = \frac{[H^+]\,[Q_{red}^{2-}]}{[HQ_{red}]} \tag{6.58c}$$

The *total* concentration of an inert wire electrode placed in a mixture of Q_{ox} and Q_{red}^{2-} is given approximately, in terms of concentrations, by

$$E_{QH} = E^{\ominus} + \frac{RT}{2F} \ln \frac{[Q_{ox}]}{[Q_{red}^{2-}]} \tag{6.59}$$

The *total* concentration of quinhydrone (present in all forms) is given by:

$$C_{red} = [H_2Q_{red}] + [HQ_{red}^-] + [Q_{red}^{2-}]$$

or, in terms of $[Q_{red}^{2-}]$ via the dissociation constants, K_1 and K_2,

$$C_{red} = \frac{[H^+]^2[Q_{red}^{2-}]}{K_1K_2} + \frac{[H^+]\,[Q_{red}^{2-}]}{K_2} + [Q_{red}^{2-}] \tag{6.60}$$

Therefore,

$$[Q_{red}^{2-}] = \frac{C_{red}K_1K_2}{([H^+]^2 + K_1[H^+] + K_1K_2)} \tag{6.61}$$

Substitution into the expression for the electrode potential gives

$$E_{QH} = E^{\ominus} + \frac{RT}{2F} \ln \frac{[Q_{ox}]}{C_{red}}$$
$$- \frac{RT}{2F} \ln K_1 K_2 + \frac{RT}{2F} \ln ([H^+]^2 + K_1[H^+] + K_1 K_2) \quad (6.62)$$

This may be simplified to

$$E_{QH} = E_{QH}^{\ominus'} + \frac{RT}{2F} \ln ([H^+]^2 + K_1[H^+] + K_1 K_2) \quad (6.63)$$

where $E_{QH}^{\ominus'}$ includes

$$E^{\ominus} + \frac{RT}{2F} \ln K_1 K_2$$

the second term in Equation (6.62) being zero, since $C_{red} = [Q_{ox}]$ for quinhydrone.

The second term of Equation (6.63) will simplify to different forms depending on the pH range used:

In *acid* solution $[H^+]^2 \gg K_1 K_2 + K_1 H^+$; therefore,

$$E_{QH} \sim E_{QH}^{\ominus'} - \frac{2 \cdot 303 RT}{F} \text{pH} \quad (6.64)$$

if

$$K_1[H^+] \gg [H^+]^2 + K_1 K_2$$

$$E_{QH} \sim E_{QH}^{\ominus'} + \frac{RT}{2F} \ln K_1 - \frac{2 \cdot 303 RT}{F} \text{pH} \quad (6.65)$$

in *alkali*, $K_1 K_2 \gg K_1 [H^+] + [H^+]^2$; therefore,

$$E_{QH} \sim E_{QH}^{\ominus'} + \frac{RT}{2F} \ln K_1 K_2 \quad (6.66)$$

(i.e. independent of pH). The first relation, Equation (6.64), holds for pH < 7; above this pH hydroquinone undergoes partial hydrolysis and atmospheric oxidation. It may not be used in oxidizing or reducing media. It is a pity that the above considerations make the quinhydrone electrode of restricted practical use, for the technique required for its use is extremely simple. It is simply required to place a small quantity of quinhydrone into the solution whose pH is required, dip an inert wire into the solution and measure the potential of the resultant half-cell with respect to a reference electrode via a potentiometer.

6.5.3   The antimony electrode

Antimony electrodes, formed by simply casting the material in air with the formation of surface oxide, behave reversibly with respect to hydrogen ions in solution according to

$$Sb_2O_3 + 6 H^+ + 6 e \rightleftharpoons 2 Sb + 3 H_2O \qquad (6.67)$$

While of little practical use as a laboratory tool, requiring calibration for any type of solution used, it has proved useful on an industrial scale for monitoring pH in plants where its robustness is a particular asset.

6.5.4   The glass electrode

The glass electrode is the most widely used indicator electrode for pH determinations used in the laboratory. It operates on the principle that the potential difference between the surface of a glass membrane and a solution is a

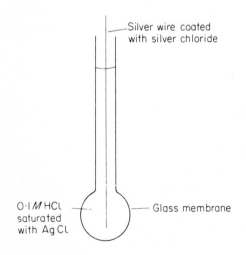

FIGURE 6.2
Essential features of the glass electrode.

linear function of pH. A standard solution of known pH must be in contact with the other side of the membrane to act as a reference electrode. The construction is shown schematically in Fig. 6.2. The arrangement may be represented as

$$\text{Ag, AgCl(s) | 0·1 } M \text{ HCl | glass | solution}$$

When used in practice it must be coupled with a reference electrode also dipping into the working solution, e.g.

$$\text{Ag, AgCl(s) | 0·1 } M \text{ HCl | glass | solution || KCl (satd.), Hg}_2\text{Cl}_2\text{ (s), Hg}$$

Since the potential of the silver–silver chloride electrode is constant and the potential difference between the *inner* surface of the glass membrane and the hydrochloric acid solution is constant, the only potential difference which can vary is that between the *outer* surface of the membrane and the working solution. The overall potential of the system is thus a function of the pH of the working solution only.

The above cell forms the basis for the *practical* pH scale which may be defined by

$$pH_X = pH_S - \frac{(E_X - E_S)F}{2 \cdot 303RT} \tag{6.88}$$

Here, pH_S represents the value for a standard buffer solution while E_S is the e.m.f. of the cell when this buffer is present. pH_X and E_X represent the pH value and cell e.m.f. respectively when the buffer solution is replaced by the solution under study. pH_S values are obtained initially by the methods previously described whereby reference electrodes are recalibrated by the use of Equation (6.56).

The mode of action of the glass electrode is very complex and, of all the theories put forward, no single one can account for all the observed properties. It is very likely, however, that an important stage involves the absorption of hydrogen ions into the lattice of the glass membrane. The potential of the glass electrode/calomel cell may be expressed as

$$E = K + \frac{RT}{F} \ln a_{H^+} \tag{6.69}$$

Here K is not a true constant but varies on a day-to-day basis for any electrode. It is for this reason that a glass electrode must always be standardized at regular intervals with buffer solutions of known pH. At least two such solutions should be used covering a range of pH values to ensure the constancy of K over this selected range. The variation of K is a function of the *asymmetry potential* of the glass electrode which is determined by the differing responses to pH of the inner and outer surfaces of the membrane. This difference may well originate in the different conditions of strain in the two surfaces.

The glass electrode works reliably in the range pH 1–9 and it is unaffected by poisoning and oxidizing and reducing agents. In alkaline solutions, at pH > 9, particularly when sodium ions are present, the pH values recorded tend to be lower than the true values and this is probably due to the infiltration of sodium ions into the glass lattice. Such 'alkaline errors' are minimized by the use of special glasses; lithium glasses, for instance, extend the range reliably to pH 12. At the acid extreme of the scale, reliability is again questionable for pH < 1, where it appears that interference from anion surface adsorption occurs.

6.6   Other ion-sensitive electrodes

The 'alkaline error' of glass membrane electrodes has been exploited in the development of electrodes sensitive to sodium and potassium ions. By analogy with the pH scale we have

$$pX = -\log a_X \qquad (6.70)$$

for an electrode responsive to a selected ion, X, whose potential may be given by

$$E = K + \frac{2 \cdot 303RT}{nF} \log a_X \qquad (6.71)$$

therefore,

$$E = K - \frac{2 \cdot 303RT}{nF} pX \qquad (6.72)$$

K representing the proportion of the total potential due to constants of the system. Changes in potential, due to changes in a_X, originate in the *outer*

138

surface of the membrane. Many ion-selective membrane materials other than glass have been developed, their response being a function of ion-exchange reactions at their surface and ion conduction inside them. There are essentially three types of membrane electrodes, viz., glass, solid state and liquid.

6.6.1 Glass membrane electrodes

It is well known that glass electrodes require soaking before use to allow certain components of the glass and the solution to exchange and produce an 'ion exchanging layer' on the membrane surface. The condition of the electrode after this operation is completed is summarized in Fig. 6.3. Water

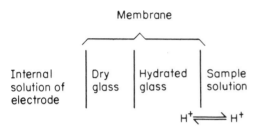

FIGURE 6.3
Schematic arrangement of a glass membrane electrode.

molecules become associated with part of the membrane and play a part in the ion-exchange process. Glass is unique in that, while it is an ionic conductor for small ions such as sodium, it is hydrogen ions which are involved most exclusively in the ion-exchange process even at high pH values and when the activity of ions such as Na^+ is high. In the latter condition the membrane shows response to these ions as evidenced by the alkaline error. Electrodes specifically intended for the determination of pNa or pK have the glass composition so devised that they show an enhanced alkaline error while at the same time having the preference for hydrogen ions in the exchange process suppressed as much as possible.

6.6.2 Solid state electrodes

Here the membrane is either a single crystal or a solid ion exchanging material. For instance, for halide ion-sensitive electrodes the membrane may be a solid silver salt, the potential of the electrode being given by

$$E = E^\ominus + \frac{2 \cdot 303RT}{F} \log a_{Ag^+} \tag{6.73}$$

At the surface of the membrane there is a certain activity of silver ions which is a function of the halide activity of the solution into which the electrode dips (Fig. 6.4).

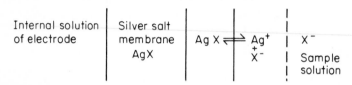

FIGURE 6.4
Arrangment of components in a solid-state ion sensitive electrode.

The activity of silver ions may be expressed in terms of the solubility product of the silver halide by

$$a_{Ag^+} = \frac{K_{AgX}}{a_{X^-}} \tag{6.74}$$

therefore,

$$E = E^\ominus + \frac{2 \cdot 303RT}{F} (\log K_{AgX} - \log a_{X^-})$$

therefore

$$E = K - \frac{2 \cdot 303RT}{F} \log a_{X^-} \tag{6.75}$$

6.6.3   Liquid membrane electrodes

A liquid membrane comprises a thin, porous inert support impregnated with an ion-exchanging material in the liquid phase. This material is often an organic species dissolved in some organic solvent, in which case use in non-aqueous solutions may be restricted. There are two types of liquid membranes; (a) charged liquid membranes which usually contain the ion for which the electrode is sensitive (the operation here is very similar to the solid state case), and (b) neutral liquid membranes which usually do not contain the ion to be detected. For instance, in the Philips liquid membrane potassium electrode, the ion exchanging species is the antibiotic valinomycin dissolved in diphenyl-ether. Potassium ions and valinomycin form a slightly water soluble complex so that the situation across the membrane may be represented by Fig. 6.5.

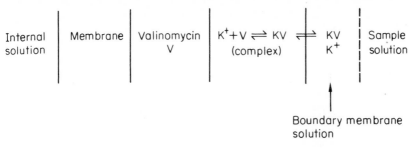

FIGURE 6.5
Arrangement of components in a liquid membrane ion-sensitive electrode.

The potential of the electrode is found to be given by the relation

$$E = K + \frac{2 \cdot 303RT}{F} \log a_{K^+} \tag{6.76}$$

The most important practical difficulty with ion-sensitive electrodes is the interference from ion species in solution other than the one required. Such electrodes must therefore be devised so that their *selectivity* for the ion in question is as high as possible. Glass electrodes for pH determination are the most selective of all ion-sensitive electrodes but we have seen that, even here, serious interferences may occur. When other ions interfere the equation for the potential adopted by the electrode must be modified to

$$E = K + \frac{2 \cdot 303RT}{nF} \log(a_i + K_{ij}a_j + K_{ik}a_k + K_{il}a_l + \cdots) \tag{6.77}$$

where a_i = activity of ion to be determined; $a_j, a_k, a_l \ldots$ = activities of inter-fering ions; and $K_{ij}, K_{ik}, K_{il} \ldots$ = 'selectivity constants' of the electrode towards particular ions. These selectivity constants are defined as follows

$$K_{ij} = \frac{u_j}{u_i} \left({}_e K_{ij} \right) \tag{6.78}$$

where u_i, u_j are ion mobilities and $_eK_{ij}$ is the equilibrium constant for the reaction

$$j_{solution} + i_{membrane} \rightleftharpoons j_{membrane} + i_{solution}$$

In cases where neutral membranes are used, the mobilities used are those of the complexes of the membrane material formed by the determined and interfering ions.

6.7 Potentiometry

Potentiometric techniques employ measurement of electrode potentials and their variation with changing chemical environment. It is less usual for electrode potentials to be used for direct concentration measurements although the most noteworthy exception is the case of hydrogen ion determination in pH measurements. Titration techniques, in which the variation of potentials during the addition of titrant is recorded, are of considerable importance and versatility.

6.7.1 Zero current potentiometry

For this technique it is simply required to have access to an indicator electrode whose potential is a function of the activity of the species to be titrated. A cell is then made by placing this indicator electrode with a suitable reference electrode in the solution to be titrated. The cell is connected in the circuit shown in Fig. 6.6 and its e.m.f. measured after each addition of titrant. Zero

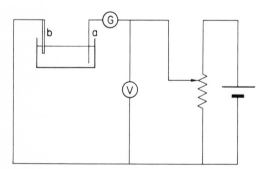

FIGURE 6.6
Basic circuit for classical potentiometry: a = indicator electrode; b = reference electrode.

current is maintained through an indicating galvanometer by balancing the cell e.m.f. against a potential divider voltage.

The equivalence point of the titration may be determined either from the inflexion point of the graph of indicator potential versus titrant volume (Fig. 6.7a) or from the derivative plot of dE/dv versus v (Fig. 6.7b).

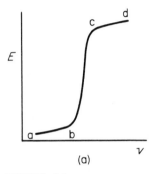 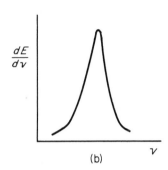

FIGURE 6.7
Potentiometric titration curves.

Although the potential versus volume plot is always of essentially the same sigmoid form, its shape is dependent upon the equilibrium constant of the titration reaction and its stoichiometry. The equivalence point may be *identified* with the inflection point for a 1 : 1 reaction with large equilibrium constant and may be satisfactorily determined for a large number of acid/ base, precipitation, redox and, in particular, complexometric titrations. Electrode reactions need not proceed reversibly for a satisfactory potentio- metric end-point to be determined. What is essential is that there shall be a large, well-defined potential change in the region of the end-point. Consider the oxidation of ferrous ions by ceric ions, a reaction already considered in section 6.4.4 where it was seen that the redox potential of the Fe^{3+}/Fe^{2+} couple (+0·77 volt) is significantly different to that of the Ce^{4+}/Ce^{3+} couple (1·61 volt). With a solution of ferrous ions placed in the cell fitted with a platinum indicator and calomel reference electrode and a burette containing a solution of ceric ions, a titration curve of the form shown in Fig. 6.7a may be obtained. As soon as a small amount of ceric solution is added to the solution of ferrous ions, some oxidation takes place, i.e.

$$Fe^{2+} + Ce^{4+} \rightarrow Fe^{3+} + Ce^{3+}$$

143

The indicator and reference electrodes are now dipping into a solution containing mainly ferrous ions but a small amount of ferric ions. The potential of the platinum electrode will now adopt a characteristic value which is a function of the activity ratio of ferric to ferrous ions as expressed in the Nernst equation.

$$E_{Fe^{3+}/Fe^{2+}} = E^{\ominus}_{Fe^{3+}/Fe^{2+}} + \frac{RT}{F} \ln \frac{a_{Fe^{3+}}}{a_{Fe^{2+}}}$$

As more ceric ions are added the ratio of ferric to ferrous ions increases. The potential adopted by the indicator electrode does not, however, vary greatly. Its value increases only slowly over the range a–b (Fig. 6.7a) in accordance with the Nernst equation. A point will be reached where all the ferrous ions have been removed by oxidation and a small excess of ceric ions have been added. The potential of the indicator electrode will now be a function of the ratio of activities of ceric and cerous ions according to

$$E_{Ce^{4+}/Ce^{3+}} = E^{\ominus}_{Ce^{4+}/Ce^{3+}} + \frac{RT}{F} \ln \frac{a_{Ce^{4+}}}{a_{Ce^{3+}}}$$

The region c–d in Fig. 6.7a shows similar slight variation of potential with titrant volume as is seen over the region a–b. The regions a–b and c–d are separated widely because of the large difference in standard potentials of the two redox systems. It is seen that in the region of the equivalence point the potential of the two couples is the same – a fact already used in section 6.4.4 to determine the equilibrium constant of the redox reaction. Between the two, virtually plateau, regions the potential shows a sharp increase.

6.7.2   *Constant (finite) current potentiometry*

Constant current techniques often prove to be useful for redox titrations involving couples of which at least one behaves in an irreversible manner, i.e., equilibrium is not established instantaneously at the electrode surface. As a result of this the potential jump in the region of the end-point is too small to be useful. The potentials of electrodes which behave irreversibly show considerable variation in value when they pass a current. The constant current required for such titrations has to be determined in a separate determination prior to the titration itself. In Fig. 6.8 are shown current–voltage curves for two redox couples one of which behaves reversibly, the other irreversibly. It is seen that at zero current the potentials are very close whereas, with increasing current, they begin to diverge considerably. In some cases the divergence can be so large that, when the titration is subsequently performed, there is no need to plot the titration graph, the end-point being directly determinable by a large change in electrode potential.

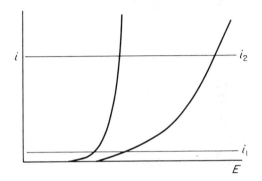

FIGURE 6.8
Current–potential curves for titrant and titrand. Constant current i_2 gives better separation of potentials than i_1.

6.7.3   Potentiometry with two indicator electrodes

When two indicator electrodes are used, the potential difference between them is plotted as a function of titrant concentration. The shapes of the individual titration curves vary with the degree of irreversibility of the couples as shown in Fig. 6.9. The titration of ferrous ion by ceric ion gives a curve of the type shown in Fig. 6.9a and the reactions occurring at various points on the curve will be briefly considered.

The most important stages of the titration occur at the points on the curve labelled 1–4.

(1) The only electroactive species present are Fe^{2+} and H_3O^+ so that the only reactions possible are

$$H_3O^+ + e \rightarrow \tfrac{1}{2}H_2 + H_2O \quad \text{at the cathode}$$

and

$$Fe^{2+} \rightarrow Fe^{3+} + e \quad \text{at the anode}$$

Since these two reactions occur at well-separated potentials, ΔE is large.

145

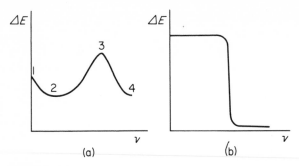

FIGURE 6.9
Potentiometric titration curves using two indicator electrodes.

(a) Both redox couples reversible.
(b) One couple reversible, the other irreversible.

(2) At this point the titration reaction is half completed, so that $[Fe^{2+}]$ = $[Fe^{3+}]$ = $[Ce^{3+}]$. Possible reactions are now

$$Fe^{3+} + e \rightarrow Fe^{2+} \quad \text{at the cathode}$$

and

or
$$\left.\begin{array}{l} Fe^{2+} \rightarrow Fe^{3+} + e \\ Ce^{3+} \rightarrow Ce^{4+} + e \end{array}\right\} \text{ at the anode.}$$

Since the second suggested anode reaction only occurs at a very positive potential it is an unlikely contribution. ΔE is now small since the cathode and anode reactions occur at almost the same potential (the ferric/ferrous couple is fairly reversible).

(3) Here the end-point has been reached; all the ferrous ion has been oxidized to the ferric state and all the ceric ion has been reduced to cerous. The electrode reactions are thus

$$Fe^{3+} + e \rightarrow Fe^{2+} \quad \text{at the cathode}$$

and

$$Ce^{3+} \rightarrow Ce^{4+} + e \quad \text{at the anode}$$

ΔE is again very large, since the latter reactions occur at widely different potentials.

146

(4) As more and more ceric ion enters the solution beyond the end-point, the reactions are likely to be

$$Ce^{4+} + e \rightarrow Ce^{3+} \qquad \text{at the cathode}$$

and

$$Ce^{3+} \rightarrow Ce^{4+} + e \quad \text{at the anode}$$

ΔE drops rapidly from the end-point to a very small value consistent with the high degree of reversibility of the ceric/cerous system.

In the case of titration of an irreversible titrand by a reversible titrant, the change of ΔE in the region of the equivalence point is shown in Fig. 6.9b. ΔE is very small after the completion of the reaction when only a reversible couple is present. This is an example of what is sometimes called a 'dead-stop' end-point.

Further reading

Bates, R.G. (1973), *Determination of pH* 2nd Edn., Wiley, New York.
Charlot, G., Badoz-hambling, J., and Tremillon, B. (1962), *Electrochemical Reactions,* Elsevier, Amsterdam.
Dole, M. (1941), *The Glass Electrode,* Wiley, New York.
Eisenman, G. (1967), *Glass Electrodes for Hydrogen and other Cations,* Arnold, London.
Rossotti, H. (1969), *Chemical Applications of Potentiometry,* Van Nostrand, New York.
Lingane, J.J. (1958), *Electroanalytical Chemistry* 2nd Edn, Interscience, New York.

Interfacial (double layer) phenomena 7

7.1 The significance of the interface between conducting phases

At the interface between any pair of conducting phases a potential difference exists whose magnitude is a function of both the composition and nature of the phases. There are many types of interface for which this phenomenon is of practical importance, e.g.,

(1) metal | electrolyte solution;
(2) metal | metal;
(3) electrolyte solution | electrolyte solution;
(4) solution of lower concentration | semipermeable membrane | solution of higher concentration.

The observed potentials are produced by the electrical double layer whose structure is responsible for many of the properties of a given system; the double layer itself arising from an excess of charges at the interface which may be ions, electrons or oriented dipoles.

Electrode kinetics, to be considered in the next chapter, are profoundly influenced by the structure of the double layer at an electrode–solution interface and it is with such systems that we shall be primarily concerned. However, double layer theory, as developed for electrode–electrolyte solution interfaces, leads on to the proper interpretation of electrokinetic phenomena, an understanding of the factors affecting colloid stability, and to the elucidation of cell membrane and ion-exchange processes.

149

7.2   The electrode double layer

Although double layers are a general interfacial phenomena, we shall first consider only electrode–electrolyte interfaces because of their importance in electrode kinetics and because the theory leads on to a general treatment of all such phenomena.

For the case of an electrode dipping into a solution of an electrolyte, we see that, for electroneutrality, the excess charge residing on the electrode surface must be exactly balanced by an equal charge of opposite sign on the solution side. It is the distribution of this latter charge that we are interested in. When only electrostatic interaction operates, ions from the solution phase may approach the electrode only so far as their inner solvation shells will allow. The surface array of ions is thus 'cushioned' from the electrode surface by a layer of solvent molecules (Fig. 7.1). The line drawn through the centre

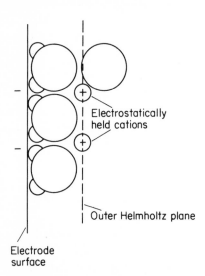

Electrostatically held cations

Outer Helmholtz plane

Electrode surface

FIGURE 7.1
The Helmholtz double layer.

of such ions at this distance of closest approach marks a boundary known as the 'outer Helmholtz plane'. The region within this plane constitutes the compact part of the double layer or the Helmholtz layer.

The size of the ions forming up *at* the outer Helmholtz plane are such that sufficient of them to neutralize the charge on the electrode cannot all fit here. The remaining charges are held with increasing disorder as the distance from the electrode surface increases, where electrostatic forces become weaker and where dispersion by thermal motion is more effective. This less ordered arrangement of charges of sign opposite to that on the electrode constitutes the *diffuse part of the double layer*. Thus, all the charge which neutralizes that on the electrode is held in a region between the outer Helmholtz plane and the bulk of the electrolyte solution. The variation of potential, ψ, with distance from the electrode surface is shown in Fig. 7.2. This is only the case

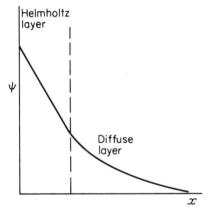

FIGURE 7.2
Variation of potential with distance from the electrode surface.

for purely electrostatic interaction between the electrode and ions in solution. In other cases *specific adsorption* of ions may occur in which van der Waals and chemical forces participate. Most anions are specifically adsorbed, thereby losing most, if not all, of their inner hydration shell. This behaviour contrasts with that of most cations, which retain their hydration molecules. Specifically adsorbed species can evidently approach much closer to the electrode surface (Fig. 7.3). A line drawn through the centres of such species aligned at the electrode surface defines a further boundary *within* the Helmholtz layer – the so-called *inner Helmholtz plane.* The extent to which specific adsorption occurs is controlled by the nature of ions in solution as

151

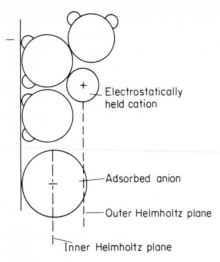

Electrostatically
held cation

Adsorbed anion

Outer Helmholtz plane

Inner Helmholtz plane

FIGURE 7.3
Relative positions of inner and outer Helmholtz planes of electrode double layer.

well as by the nature of the electrode material and the potential applied to it.

Uncharged species, if they are less polar than the solvent or are attracted to the electrode material by van der Waals or chemical forces, will accumulate at the interface. Such species are known as *surfactants*. Where specific adsorption occurs, the charge distribution in the diffuse layer will change to maintain electroneutrality.

7.3   Polarized and non-polarized electrodes

The ideal non-polarized electrode is one which allows free and unimpeded exchange of electrons or ions across the electrode–solution interface. The reversible electrodes considered in an earlier chapter approximate in behaviour to these, the rapid establishment of thermodynamic equilibrium being consequent upon such rapid interchange. When charge crosses an ideally reversible electrode, the electrochemical changes which take place do so with such rapidity that the equilibrium situation is instantaneously restored. Such an electrode is *non-polarizable* in the sense that its potential, for small currents, has remained stable. This potential, for a fixed temperature and pressure, is governed solely by the activities of the electrode constituents and species in solution. The potential of a silver electrode, for example, is determined under constant external conditions *only* by the activity of silver ions in solution.

The *ideal polarized electrode*, on the other hand, allows *no* movement of charges between the phases. The potential adopted by such an electrode may be varied at will by altering its charge through variation of applied potential, without affecting the equilibrium condition at the interface. Such a system is equivalent to a perfect condenser without leakage and, like a perfect condenser, it may be charged by connection to a reference electrode and source of e.m.f. and will then retain the impressed potential when the source is removed. In practice this behaviour is very difficult to attain but the mercury electrode in potassium chloride solution approaches very closely to the behaviour required of an ideal polarized electrode. Within a certain range of potentials, ions are not discharged at its surface, neither are they dissolved from it, so that the potential may be varied *without* the establishment of electrochemical equilibrium. Possible reactions which might occur are:

$K^+ + e \rightleftharpoons K$ (amalgam) – since the concentration of potassium in the amalgam is extremely low, this reaction can only occur to a minute extent;

$2 Hg \rightleftharpoons Hg_2^{2+} + 2 e$ – again, this could only be expected to occur to a very smal extent because of the small equilibrium concentration of mercurous ions;

$2 Cl^- \rightleftharpoons Cl_2 + 2 e$ – due to the partial pressure of chlorine being so low, this reaction is unlikely;

$2 H_2O + 2 e \rightleftharpoons H_2 + 2 OH^-$ – this reaction is unlikely, due to the high hydrogen overvoltage on mercury (see next chapter).

In practice, therefore, a near-ideal polarized electrode may be identified by the fact that, over a range of applied potential, no current flows. A *polarized* electrode shows no current *change* over a range of applied potential, i.e., a *finite* current flows but is limited to a constant value over a range of applied potential.

7.4 The diffuse double layer

This portion is controlled solely by electrostatic forces, the distribution of ions in relation to the charged electrode surface is a function of their charge and valency. It is a very similar problem to that solved by the Debye–Hückel theory for the three-dimensional distribution of ion species in solution, except that, with interfacial phenomena at a planar electrode, we need only consider a one-dimensional situation, i.e., we need only consider variation of potential in one direction normal to the electrode surface. It is necessary to remember that such a treatment applied to the present problem will give an expression for the potential at an *effective surface,* i.e. at the outer Helmholtz plane (Fig. 7.4).

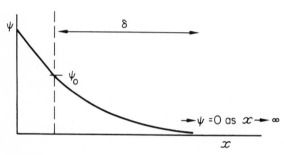

FIGURE 7.4
The diffuse double layer in the region bounded by the conditions $\psi = \psi_0$ and $\psi = 0$.

For a single (x) direction we may write, by analogy with Equation (2.10)

$$\frac{\partial^2 \psi}{\partial x^2} = \frac{e^2 \psi}{\varepsilon_0 \varepsilon \, kT} \, \Sigma N_i z_i^{\ 2} = \kappa^2 \psi = \frac{\rho}{\varepsilon_0 \varepsilon} \tag{7.1}$$

whereas $1/\kappa$ in the Debye–Hückel theory is regarded as the effective radius of the ion atmosphere about an ion, here it is to be identified with δ the thickness of the diffuse double layer. For Equation (7.1) the general solution follows by analogy with that for (2.12), viz.,

$$\psi = A \, e^{-\kappa x} + B \, e^{\kappa x} \tag{7.2}$$

and since $\psi \to 0$ as $x \to 0$, $B = 0$. Now,

$$\frac{-\rho}{\varepsilon_0 \varepsilon} = \kappa^2 \psi$$

154

where ρ = charge/unit volume of electrolyte solution. Therefore,

$$\rho = - \varepsilon_0 \varepsilon \, \kappa^2 \, \psi \tag{7.3}$$

$$= -A \varepsilon_0 \varepsilon \, \kappa^2 \, e^{-\kappa x} \tag{7.4}$$

(by combining Equations (7.2) and (7.3)).

Let the charge density at the electrode surface (i.e. at $x = 0$) be σ/unit area. This then is equal in magnitude, but of opposite sign, to the *total* volume charge in solution, i.e.,

$$\sigma = - \int_a^\infty \rho \, dx \tag{7.5}$$

a being the distance of closest approach of ions to the surface. Therefore,

$$\sigma = -A \varepsilon_0 \varepsilon \, \kappa^2 \int_a^\infty e^{-\kappa x} dx \tag{7.6}$$

$$= A \varepsilon_0 \varepsilon \, \kappa \, e^{-\kappa a} \tag{7.7}$$

therefore,

$$A = \frac{\sigma}{\varepsilon_0 \varepsilon \kappa} e^{\kappa a} \tag{7.8}$$

When this latter expression for A is substituted into that for ψ Equation (7.2), we obtain

$$\psi = \frac{\sigma}{\varepsilon_0 \varepsilon \, \kappa} e^{\kappa (a - x)} \tag{7.9}$$

In the condition that x approaches a, i.e. the outer limit of the Helmholtz layer, $(a - x) \to 0$. Under these conditions ψ will be designated ψ_0; i.e.

$$\psi_0 = \frac{\sigma}{\varepsilon_0 \varepsilon \, \kappa} = \zeta \tag{7.10}$$

ψ_0 may, for our present purposes, be identified with ζ (the 'zeta' potential) i.e. the potential at the point where the potential difference across the interface ceases to be uniform viz., the edge of the outer Helmholtz layer where the diffuse layer begins.

The capacity, C_D, of the (electrolyte concentration dependent) diffuse layer is given by

$$C_D = \frac{\sigma}{\zeta} = \varepsilon_0 \varepsilon \kappa$$

therefore

$$\zeta = \frac{\sigma \delta}{\varepsilon_0 \varepsilon} \tag{7.11}$$

This equation forms the basis for the explanation and description of all electrokinetic phenomena.

There are effectively *two* components which make up the total potential drop across the interface; viz., ψ_0 across the diffuse part, and $(\psi - \psi_0)$ across the fixed part. The total capacitance of the double layer, C, is made up of that due to the inner (adsorption) layer, which we may designate C_H, and that due to the diffuse layer, C_D. Since these capacitances are connected in series

$$\frac{1}{C} = \frac{1}{C_H} + \frac{1}{C_D}$$

or,

$$C = \frac{C_H C_D}{C_H + C_D} \tag{7.12}$$

Now, if the electrolyte solution is very dilute, $C_D \ll C_H$ and $C \approx C_D$. The double layer is now essentially all *diffuse*, and this was the model adopted by Gouy and Chapman in their work on the double layer. On the other hand, when the solution is very concentrated $C_D \gg C_H$ and $C \approx C_H$, which defines the earliest model of the double layer due to Helmholtz.

7.5 Electrocapillarity

Interfacial tension measurements on liquid metal electrodes, such as mercury, have provided a great deal of information about double layer structure and have indicated the factors governing adsorption at a charged interface. The interfacial tension, γ, of a mercury/solution interface may be observed with the Lippmann electrometer, which is shown schematically in Fig. 7.5. The mercury meets the solution in a fine-bore capillary, the meniscus being observed by means of a microscope. If a potential is applied to the mercury,

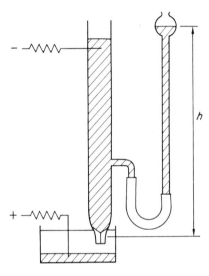

FIGURE 7.5
Principle of the Lippmann electrometer.

the position of the meniscus is seen to change but may be restored to its original position by changing the reservoir height, h. The amount by which h is required to be changed is a function of the change in interfacial tension caused by the applied potential. Mercury takes up a positive charge with respect to an aqueous solution; when a small negative potential is applied, some of this charge is neutralized and the interfacial tension rises. A point is reached where all the positive charge is neutralized and γ will then reach its maximum value. As an excess of negative charge is added with further increase in negative potential, γ will again decrease (Fig. 7.6).

The dependence of interfacial tension upon applied potential may be derived by application of the Gibbs adsorption isotherm to the system of

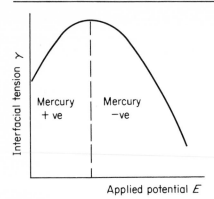

FIGURE 7.6
Schematic variation of interfacial tension with applied potential (electrocapillary curve) for a mercury-aqueous electrolyte solution interface.

phases in equilibrium in an electrochemical cell incorporating an almost *ideal* polarized electrode.

The Gibbs adsorption isotherm is expressed in the form

$$d\gamma + \sum \Gamma_i \, d\mu_i = 0 \tag{7.13}$$

where γ is the interfacial tension between two phases and Γ_i is the interfacial concentration of adsorbed species, i, this latter being neutral so that its chemical potential, μ_i, is a function of the pressure, temperature and composition of the phase.

We are concerned, however, with charged species. When i carries charge its chemical potential is also a function of the *electrical potential*, ψ, of the phase in which it exists. Thus, for ions of charge n_i, we define the *electrochemical potential*, $\tilde{\mu}_i$, by

$$\tilde{\mu}_i = \mu_i + n_i F \psi \tag{7.14}$$

So that, for ions, the Gibbs adsorption isotherm is expressed in terms of electrochemical potential by

$$d\gamma + \sum \Gamma_i \, d\tilde{\mu}_i = 0 \tag{7.15}$$

158

Equation (7.15) tells us that the interfacial tension depends upon the electrical potential difference between the phases. For instance, in a metal–electrolyte solution system, γ is a function of the electrode potential.

Let us apply Equation (7.15) to the following cell, comprising *four* distinct phases

$$Pt(H_2) \mid HCl \mid Hg \mid Pt$$
$$\quad 1 \quad\quad 2 \quad\; 3 \quad 4$$

in which we regard the hydrogen electrode as non-polarizable and the mercury electrode as ideally polarizable.

From Equation (7.15) we have for the interface between phase 2 and phase 3,

$$-d\gamma = [\Gamma_{Hg^+} d\tilde{\mu}_{Hg^+} + \Gamma_{e^-} d\tilde{\mu}_{e^-}]$$
$$+ [\Gamma_{H_3O^+} d\tilde{\mu}_{H_3O^+} + \Gamma_{Cl^-} d\tilde{\mu}_{Cl^-} + \Gamma_{H_2O} d\mu_{H_2O}] \quad (7.16)$$

Now, for an electrolyte, the chemical potential is the sum of the potentials of its component ions, e.g.,

$$\mu = \nu_+\mu_+ + \nu_-\mu_- \quad (7.17)$$

therefore,

$$\mu_{Hg} = \tilde{\mu}_{Hg^+} + \tilde{\mu}_{e^-} \quad \text{in phase 3}$$

and $\quad\quad\quad\quad\quad\quad\quad\quad\quad\quad\quad\quad\quad\quad\quad\quad\quad\quad (7.18)$

$$\mu_{HCl} = \tilde{\mu}_{H_3O^+} + \tilde{\mu}_{Cl^-} \quad \text{in phase 2}$$

therefore,

$$-d\gamma = [\Gamma_{Hg^+} d\mu_{Hg} - (\Gamma_{Hg^+} - \Gamma_{e^-}) d\tilde{\mu}_{e^-}]$$
$$+ [\Gamma_{Cl^-} d\mu_{HCl} + (\Gamma_{H_3O^+} - \Gamma_{Cl^-}) d\tilde{\mu}_{H_3O^+} + \Gamma_{H_2O} d\mu_{H_2O}] \quad (7.19)$$

Now

$$\Gamma_i = \frac{n_i}{A} \quad (7.20)$$

159

i.e. the number of particles of species i per unit area. We can therefore express the total number of charges per unit area, absorbed by the interface from phase 2 and phase 3 as

$$(\Gamma_{Hg^+} - \Gamma_{e^-})F = \sigma_3$$

and

$$\left.\begin{array}{c}\\ \\ \end{array}\right\} \qquad (7.21)$$

$$(\Gamma_{H_3O^+} - \Gamma_{Cl^-})F = \sigma_2$$

For electroneutrality at the interface

$$\sigma_2 + \sigma_3 = 0 \qquad (7.22)$$

Also, for equilibrium to be maintained across the interface between mercury and platinum (phase 3 and phase 4)

$$(d\tilde{\mu}_{e^-})_3 = (d\tilde{\mu}_{e^-})_4 \qquad (7.23)$$

Similarly, for equilibrium across the interface between phases 1 and 2,

$$(d\tilde{\mu}_{H_3O^+})_2 = -(d\tilde{\mu}_{e^-})_1 \qquad (7.24)$$

Substituting Equations (7.21)–(7.24) into Equation (7.19) yields

$$-d\gamma = \Gamma_{Hg^+}\, d\mu_{Hg} - \frac{\sigma_3}{F}\left(d\tilde{\mu}_{e^-}\right)_4 + \Gamma_{Cl^-}\, d\mu_{HCl}$$

$$+ \frac{\sigma_2}{F}\left(d\tilde{\mu}_{e^-}\right)_1 + \Gamma_{H_2O}\, d\mu_{H_2O} \qquad (7.25)$$

therefore

$$-d\gamma = \Gamma_{Hg^+}\, d\mu_{Hg} - \frac{\sigma_3}{F}\left[(d\tilde{\mu}_{e^-})_4 - (d\tilde{\mu}_{e^-})_1\right]$$

$$+ \Gamma_{Cl^-}\, d\mu_{HCl} + \Gamma_{H_2O}\, d\mu_{H_2O} \qquad (7.26)$$

We may assume the equality of σ_2 and σ_3 since, as the mercury electrode is completely polarizable, no charge may be transferred across the interface; for the same reason the compositions of the phases must remain constant so that $d\mu$ terms = 0.

Now, at a given temperature and pressure, the potential of the hydrogen electrode is affected only by the activity of HCl and is not affected by an applied external voltage, E. Any variations, dE in E, may therefore be regarded as changes $d(\Delta\psi)$ at the Hg/HCl interface. Therefore,

$$(d\tilde{\mu}_{e^-})_1 - (d\tilde{\mu}_{e^-})_4 = F(\psi_1 - \psi_4) = F\, dE \qquad (7.27)$$

therefore, Equation (7.26) becomes

$$-d\gamma = \Gamma_{Hg^+}\, d\mu_{Hg} + \Gamma_{Cl^-}\, d\mu_{HCl} + \Gamma_{H_2O}\, d\mu_{H_2O} + \sigma_3\, dE \qquad (7.28)$$

or,

$$\left(\frac{\partial\gamma}{\partial E}\right)_{P,T,\mu} = -\sigma_3 \qquad (7.29)$$

Equation (7.29) is known as the Lippman equation.

If we write $\sigma = CE$, where C is the capacitance of the double layer regarded as a condenser, then, at constant T, P and μ,

$$d\gamma = -CE\, dE \qquad (7.30)$$

which, on integration, gives

$$\gamma = -\frac{C}{2}E^2 + \text{constant} \qquad (7.31)$$

This last equation is seen to be a form of the equation to a parabola. At the maximum of the curve

$$\left(\frac{\partial\gamma}{\partial E}\right) = 0; \qquad \sigma = 0; \qquad E = 0.$$

Electrocapillary curves obtained with the Lippmann electrometer are not usually parabolic. For a few electrolytes, such as potassium nitrate (and even then within a limited concentration range) parabolic curves are found but more usually the curves show varying degrees of distortion. Such behaviour is always found with cations and anions which are specifically adsorbed.

The capacity of the double layer formed at the interface may be found by differentiating the Lippmann equation.

$$\left(\frac{\partial^2\gamma}{\partial E^2}\right)_{P,T,\mu} = -\frac{\partial\sigma}{\partial E} = C \qquad (7.32)$$

161

Were C to be a constant for a given electrode, identical electrocapillary curves would be obtained whatever the electrolyte dissolved in solution. Alkali metal nitrates *do* show almost identical parabolas, but other salts of given alkali metals each give their own characteristic curves (Fig. 7.7).

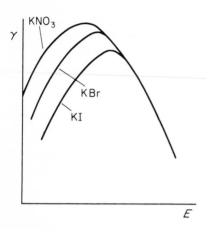

FIGURE 7.7
Effect on electrocapillary curves of specific adsorption of anions.

It is seen that the variations in electrocapillary curves for such salts occur only on the part of the curves which correspond to a positive charge being carried by the mercury electrode. Such variations are regarded as arising from specific adsorption of the various anions into the double layer. Surface active cations similarly affect the side of the curve which corresponds to mercury adopting a negative charge. Non-electrolytes which are surface active, such as gelatin, also modify the shape of electrocapillary curves – often quite drastically – and this will be seen to be of significance in the technique of polarography to be considered in Chapter 8.

7.6   Electrokinetic phenomena

Electrokinetic properties are associated with phases in contact with each other and are of particular significance for colloidal systems, although by no means restricted to these. Imposition of e.m.f.'s across such interfaces causes movements of the phases with respect to one another while forced movement of the phases produces characteristic e.m.f.'s. Thus cause and effect are readily interchangeable. Electrokinetic effects may be summarized as follows:

Motion caused by imposed e.m.f.	e.m.f. produced by movement of phases
Electro-osmosis – liquid caused to move through a static diaphragm	*Streaming potential* – potential produced by liquid being forced through a diaphragm
Electrophoresis – solid particles caused to move through a stationary liquid	*Sedimentation potential* – potential produced by the free fall of particles through a liquid (the Dorn effect)

We shall only consider electro-osmosis, streaming potential and electrophoresis in any detail.

7.6.1   Electro-osmosis

A diaphragm through which liquid is forced may be regarded as comprising a series of capillaries around the internal surface of which there exists a double layer of separated charges (Fig. 7.8).

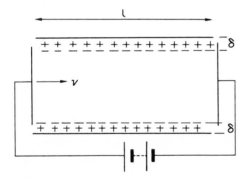

FIGURE 7.8
Cylindrically symmetrical double layer around the surface of a capillary.

Let it be assumed that, during the movement of liquid through such a capillary, the fall of velocity is confined to the double layer by frictional forces. The velocity gradient in the layer is then v/δ, while the potential gradient down the length of the tube is $E/l = V$ (V m^{-1}).

If the surface charge per unit area is σ, then the electrical force per unit area $= V\sigma$. The viscous force per unit area $= \eta\,(v/\delta)$, η being the coefficient of viscosity of the liquid. If liquid flows through the capillaries at a constant rate the electrical force balances the viscous force, i.e.

$$\eta \cdot \frac{v}{\delta} = V\sigma \tag{7.33}$$

therefore,

$$\sigma = \frac{\eta}{V} \cdot \frac{v}{\delta} \tag{7.34}$$

Now

$$\zeta = \frac{\delta}{\varepsilon_0 \varepsilon} \cdot \sigma \quad \text{(see Equation (7.11))}$$

therefore,

$$\zeta = \frac{\eta v}{\varepsilon_0 \varepsilon\, V} \quad \text{or} \quad v = \frac{\zeta \varepsilon_0 \varepsilon\, V}{\eta} \tag{7.35a}$$

For a potential gradient of 1 V m^{-1}, v is identified with u_0 the electro-osmotic mobility. Therefore,

$$\zeta = \frac{\eta\, u_0}{\varepsilon_0 \varepsilon} \tag{7.35b}$$

or,

$$u_0 = \frac{\zeta \varepsilon_0 \varepsilon}{\eta} \tag{7.35c}$$

Equations (7.35a)–(7.35c) are all forms of the Smoluchowski equation. If the volume flow per unit time and the cross-sectional area of *all* capillaries are ϕ and q respectively, then

$$v = \frac{\phi}{q} \tag{7.36}$$

and

$$\zeta = \frac{\eta \phi}{\varepsilon_0 \varepsilon\, q} \tag{7.37}$$

and, since for a single capillary, $q = \pi r^2$,

$$\phi = \frac{\zeta \varepsilon_0 \varepsilon \, V \pi r^2}{\eta} \qquad (7.38)$$

or,

$$\zeta = \frac{\eta \phi}{\varepsilon_0 \varepsilon \, V \pi r^2} \qquad (7.39)$$

Thus Equation (7.39) may be used to determine the zeta potential from measurements of ϕ, r and V. Since it is often by no means easy to measure V precisely, it is better to measure the current flowing, i, and the conductivity of the liquid, κ, and to replace V in Equation (7.39) by $i/q\kappa$. Thus,

$$\zeta = \frac{\eta \phi}{\varepsilon_0 \varepsilon \, Vq} = \frac{\eta \phi \kappa}{\varepsilon_0 \varepsilon i} \qquad (7.40)$$

It is also possible to determine ζ from measurements on a single capillary, for under these conditions the Poiseuille equation may be used, viz.

$$\phi = \frac{\pi P r^4}{8 \eta l}$$

where P is the driving pressure. This equation may be substituted into Equation (7.39), the significance of P now being the difference in pressure at the ends of the capillary resulting from electro-osmotic flow, i.e.

$$P = \frac{8 \varepsilon_0 \varepsilon \, Vl}{r^2} \qquad (7.41)$$

7.6.2 Streaming potential

The velocity of a liquid flowing in a capillary varies with the distance from the centre of the tube as shown in Fig. 7.9. The liquid at the surface of the tube is stationary so that the double layer at the interface consists of a stationary and a moving part. It is the relative movement of these two planes of the double layer which gives rise to the streaming potential. The velocity of the liquid at any point on the parabolic front distant x from the wall is given by

$$u = \frac{P(r^2 - x^2)}{4 \eta l} \qquad (7.42)$$

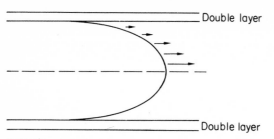

Double layer

Double layer

FIGURE 7.9
Variation of liquid velocity through a capillary with distance from the centre.

Thus, the moving part of the double layer, at a distance $(r - \delta)$ from the centre of the tube, moves with a velocity u_δ given by

$$u_\delta = \frac{P}{4\eta l} (r^2 - (r - \delta)^2)$$

$$= \frac{P}{4\eta l} (2r\delta - \delta^2)$$

therefore,

$$u_\delta \approx \frac{Pr\delta}{2\eta l} \quad \text{since } \delta^2 \ll 2r\delta \qquad (7.43)$$

As the movement of the front of liquid forces one layer of charges past the other, a current is produced which must be given by the product of the total charge around a unit length of tube and the velocity of the moving part of the layer, i.e.

$$i = 2\pi r \sigma u_\delta \qquad (7.44)$$

which, on substitution for u_δ from Equation (7.43) becomes

$$i = \frac{\pi r^2 \sigma \delta P}{\eta l} \qquad (7.45)$$

If the liquid has conductivity κ, the conductance of the liquid in the capillary is $\pi r^2 \kappa / l$ and its resistance $l / \pi r^2 \kappa$. Thus, by Ohm's law

$$E_S = \frac{il}{\pi r^2 \kappa}$$

where E_S is the streaming potential.

so that

$$E_S = \frac{\sigma \delta P}{\eta \kappa} \quad \text{(by substitution for } il \text{ from Equation (7.45))}$$

but

$$\zeta = \frac{\sigma \delta}{\varepsilon_0 \varepsilon} \text{ (see Equation (7.11))}.$$

from which

$$\sigma \delta = \zeta \varepsilon_0 \varepsilon$$

so that

$$E_S = \frac{\sigma \varepsilon_0 \varepsilon P}{\eta \kappa} \tag{7.46}$$

It is seen from a comparison of Equations (7.40) and (7.46) that

$$\frac{E_S}{P} = \frac{\phi}{i} \tag{7.47}$$

Equation (7.47) has indeed been experimentally verified.

7.6.3 Electrophoresis

Here solid particles, which may be of colloidal dimensions or even larger, are caused to move through a static solvent under the influence of an electric field. The electrophoretic velocity, v, in a field V is given by

$$v = \frac{\zeta \varepsilon_0 \varepsilon V}{\eta} \text{ (see Equation (7.35a))}$$

where it is assumed that the thickness of the double layer is small in comparison with the size of the particles.

The velocity attained by an ion moving in the field is

$$v = \frac{z_i \epsilon V}{R} \tag{7.48}$$

where R is the viscous resistance to the motion of the ion given by Stokes' law for a spherical particle of radius r by

$$R = 6\pi\eta r$$

therefore,

$$v = \frac{z_i \epsilon V}{6\pi\eta r} \tag{7.49}$$

Now, such particles experience the electrophoretic and relaxation effects. To discuss the electrophoretic effect, we assume that each particle is surrounded by a diffuse double layer of a thickness dependent upon the concentrations of ions in the solution. During migration through a solution a particle drags with it a layer of liquid of thickness d (say) – d is usually less than δ. Within this layer there are a number of ions and their presence modifies the effective charge on the moving particle. If the *effective* charge is Δz, Equation (7.49) may be written as

$$v = \frac{\Delta z V}{6\pi\eta(r + d)} \tag{7.50}$$

For a spherical condenser we have, from Equation (7.11)

$$C = \frac{\Delta z}{\zeta}$$

also,

$$C = (r + d)\,4\pi\varepsilon_0\varepsilon$$

for the spherical condenser of radius $(r + d)$; therefore,

$$\Delta z = 4\pi\varepsilon_0\varepsilon\,\zeta\,(r + d) \tag{7.51}$$

From Equations (7.50) and (7.51) we obtain

$$v = \frac{\varepsilon_0\varepsilon\zeta V}{(3/2)\eta} \tag{7.52}$$

It is seen that Equation (7.52) is of the same form as Equation (7.35a) but contains a different numerical factor.

In solutions of high ionic concentration, i.e., the condition where a very thin double layer is formed, Equation (7.35a) is expected to apply. On the other hand, in very dilute solutions Equation (7.52) will be the more likely form. Corrections for the relaxation effect are rather difficult to assess for large particles on account of the Onsager correction only being applicable to cases where a central ion is small in comparison with its atmosphere.

The determination of electrophoretic velocities may be carried out experimentally by the use of methods suitable for transport number measurements. Moving boundary techniques have proved useful despite the problem of a difficulty in selecting suitable indicator ions. Reliable estimates of electrophoretic velocities make possible the determination of zeta-potentials. Since colloids migrate at characteristic rates under the influence of an electric field, electrophoresis provides an important means of separation. Coatings, such as rubber or graphite, may be deposited on metal electrodes by this means and additives to these may be co-deposited.

Of particular importance is the separation and purification of proteins. Ampholytic protein particles migrate in an electric field at a rate which is characteristic, not only of their surface properties and charge and composition of the solution, but also of the pH. This is because the charge which the particles acquire by their own loss or gain of protons is a function of pH. At a given pH, different proteins are thus dissociated to different extents and have characteristic mobilities. An originally sharp boundary between a buffer solution containing various proteins and another buffer solution without proteins, splits into several boundaries corresponding to each species. A purified protein shows a characteristic variation of migration velocity with pH – the so-called 'mobility curve'. The velocity has a different sign on either side of the isoelectric point and is zero at this point. The slope of the velocity versus pH plot at the isoelectric point is a characteristic of a given protein.

7.7   The behaviour of colloidal systems

7.7.1   Stability of colloidal dispersions

The stability of colloid particles is attributed to the nature of the double layer which exists at the interface between their surfaces and the solution in which

169

they are dispersed. Breakdown of colloidal systems, i.e., aggregation or floc-culation, is similarly caused by changes in the double layer structure.

We are here concerned with lyophobic colloids. Lyophilic colloid systems, on account of their affinity for the solvent, form thermodynamically stable solvated systems. Lyophobic colloids, on the other hand, are in a state of unstable equilibrium with the medium and are susceptible to irreversible breakdown when the equilibrium is subjected to even small disturbances. Lyophobic colloid particles carry similar charges, as may be confirmed by the direction of their migration in an electric field, and these usually originate from the preferential adsorption of ions from the solution. For example, negatively charged hydrosulphide ions are adsorbed at the surface of colloidal particles of arsenious sulphide. Consequently, the diffuse double layer, sur-rounding each particle, must contain an equivalent number of positively charged (hydrogen) ions – the 'counter ions' or 'gegen-ions'.

The repulsive forces between such particles are usually large due to the fairly large number of unit charges which each carries. Not only are the forces of repulsion large, they are of long range in comparison with the short-range attractive (dispersion) forces. The overriding repulsive forces prevent the particles aggregating, and their magnitude controls the stability of the colloid system. The magnitude of these forces may be changed by changing the num-ber of charges carried by the particles. Adsorption of oppositely charged ions, leading to partial or complete neutralization of those on the particles, reduces the repulsive forces, allows more free play of the attractive van der Waals forces and, if occurring to a sufficiently large extent, results in aggregation. The observed effects of adding electrolytes to lyophobic colloid systems are qualitatively in agreement with this interpretation, so that, for instance, the higher the charges carried by the ions of an added electrolyte, the more efficient it is found to be and the lower the concentration required to induce aggregation.

7.7.2   Colloidal electrolytes

Some electrolytes containing large ions, particularly soaps, dyes and many synthetic detergents, behave as normal electrolytes only in very dilute sol-ution. At higher concentrations they show unusually low osmotic pressures and their conductivities show large deviations from the Onsager relationship.

Such behaviour may be attributed to the formation of *micelles* by aggregation of similarly charged ions. This process of micelle formation occurs at a critical concentration for each system and is encouraged by large ion size. For example, cetylpyridinium salts show the Onsager dependence of molar conductivity on the square root of electrolyte concentration at very low concentrations ($10^{-3} M$). Beyond a critical concentration, however, the conductivity declines very rapidly and ultimately assumes a minimum almost constant value. Micelle formation, caused by the aggregation of about 68 cetylpyridinium ions, causes the observed drop in conductivity. In these micelles the cations are arranged with the cationic groups facing the solvent and with the hydrocarbon chains pointing inwards. The gegen-ions contained in the double layer surrounding the particles then reduce the latter's effective charge and mobility and give rise to the sharp drop in conductivity. With a knowledge of the transport numbers of cation and anion over the concentration range, the ion conductivities may be calculated. The conductivity of the cetylpyridinium ion increases sharply beyond the critical concentration due to the increased mobility of the hydrocarbon chain constituent. There is lower frictional resistance offered to the movement of the micelle than to that of the total number of original individual particles, and this more than outweighs the effects of the more dense ion atmosphere due to the increased concentration of charges in the micelle.

After the critical concentration the conductivity of the anion is observed to drop very sharply to zero and to pass into negative values. This is the same type of transport number behaviour as that shown by cadmium iodide (Chapter 2) and indicates that the anions are preferentially transported to the *cathode* rather than to the *anode.* It is evident that ion association between anions and positively charged micelles is the cause. Hartley calculated that in cetylpyridinium bromide about 53 bromide ions are associated with each micelle of 68 cationic species to give a net charge of $+15$.

7.7.3 *Polyelectrolytes*

Micelle particles are usually spherical in shape due to the fact that the constituent ions tend to orientate themselves with lyophobic fragments pointing inwards away from the solvent. Consequently the distribution of charge will tend to be spherically symmetrical. Polyelectrolytes, by contrast, are long-chain polymeric species which carry ionizable groups along the chain. Depending on their proximity to one another, charged groups along such a chain interact and the extent of interaction may be affected by changing the conditions of the system. Thus, in a dilute solution of sodium polymethacrylate, the repulsion between neighbouring carboxylate groups causes almost complete extension of the chain. In the parent acid, however, which is weak with ionization of the acid groups occurring to only a small extent, the chain is coiled. The coils open when alkali is added to neutralize the acid groups and increase the number of carboxylate repulsions. The addition of other salts to solutions of the fully extended poly salt causes the latter to recoil due to the increased ionic strength which reduces the inter-group repulsions.

Measurements of conductance and transport numbers similar to those used for micelles confirm the importance of association of counter ions for polyelectrolytes. An interesting feature is that in an electric field such poly ions exhibit abnormally high induced dipoles. It is apparent that the associated counter-ions have considerable mobility along the length of the chain so that the field causes polarization and orientation of the chain along the field direction.

7.8   Membrane equilibria

We consider here two solutions with different concentrations of electrolyte and non-electrolyte species separated by a membrane. This membrane allows passage of solvent molecules and most ion species, but prevents passage of at least *one* ionic species. In practice all diffusible species capable of passing through the membrane will do so, their concentrations in the solutions on either side of the membrane reaching equilibrium values after a time. The concentration of the species which cannot pass the membrane must, of course, remain constant. In this situation it is found, when equilibrium has been established, that an osmotic pressure difference is set up across the boundary between the two solutions associated with an unequal distribution of diffusible material. Further, a potential difference – the *membrane potential* – is observed across the membrane.

Consider the simple system in which an aqueous solution of a salt containing R^+ and X^- ions is separated from an aqueous solution of the acid HX by a membrane which is impermeable to R^+. If we label the two solutions I and II we may represent the initial and equilibrium situations in the following way

I	II		I		II
$H_3O^+X^-$	R^+X^-		H_3O^+	$\rightleftharpoons$	H_3O^+
H_2O	H_2O		X^-	$\rightleftharpoons$	X^-
					R^+
			H_2O	$\rightleftharpoons$	H_2O
Initial state			Equilibrium state		

R^+ cannot diffuse through the membrane on account of its size but H_3O^+ and X^- will pass through the membrane until equilibrium is achieved. In this state we have the condition $H_3O^+ = X^-$ for solution I to the left of the membrane. In solution II, however, the X^- anions must electrically balance both H_3O^+ *and* R^+.

At equilibrium, we have the following relationships for the three diffusible species

$$^I\tilde{\mu}_{H_3O^+} = {}^{II}\tilde{\mu}_{H_3O^+}; \qquad ^I\tilde{\mu}_{X^-} = {}^{II}\tilde{\mu}_{X^-}; \qquad ^I\mu_{H_2O} = {}^{II}\mu_{H_2O} \quad (7.53)$$

Where $\tilde{\mu}$ and μ represent electrochemical and chemical potentials respectively.

Since the membrane is not permeable to R^+, the pressure of the two phases will differ and it is necessary to allow for the variation of chemical potential with pressure, $(\partial\mu_i/\partial P)_T = V_i$. The chemical potential of species i is related to its activity a_i by

$$\mu_i = \mu_i^{\ominus} + RT \ln a_i \quad (7.54)$$

Now, $\mu_i^{\ominus}$, which occurs in both electrochemical and chemical potentials, may be expressed as

$$\mu_i^{\ominus} = \mu_i^* + \int_0^p V^{\ominus}\, dp \quad (7.55)$$

Where μ_i^* is the value corresponding to $p = 0$ and $V^{\ominus}$ is the molar volume in the standard state. If, as an approximation, we neglect the compressibility of the solution, we may write $V^{\ominus} = V = $ constant. Thus

$$\mu_i^{\ominus} = \mu_i^* + V_p \quad (7.56)$$

173

and

$$\mu_i = \mu_i^* + V_p + RT \ln a_i \tag{7.57}$$

Therefore, for water, acting as solvent in this case,

$$^I\mu_{H_2O} = {}^I\mu_{H_2O}^* + V_{H_2O}p^I + RT \ln {}^Ia_{H_2O} \tag{7.58}$$

and

$$^{II}\mu_{H_2O} = {}^{II}\mu_{H_2O}^* + V_{H_2O}p^{II} + RT \ln {}^{II}a_{H_2O} \tag{7.59}$$

Therefore,

$$V_{H_2O}(p^I - p^{II}) = RT \ln \frac{{}^{II}a_{H_2O}}{{}^Ia_{H_2O}} \tag{7.60}$$

Using Equations (7.14) and (7.60) we may then write for the ionic diffusible species

$$(p^I - p^{II})V_{H_3O^+} = RT \ln \frac{{}^{II}a_{H_3O^+}}{{}^Ia_{H_3O^+}} + F(\psi^{II} - \psi^I) \tag{7.61}$$

and

$$(p^I - p^{II})V_{X^-} = RT \ln \frac{{}^{II}a_{X^-}}{{}^Ia_{X^-}} - F(\psi^{II} - \psi^I) \tag{7.62}$$

Where $(\psi^{II} - \psi^I) = \Delta\psi$ the membrane potential.

Eliminating the membrane potential between Equations (7.61) and (7.62) we obtain

$$(p^I - p^{II}) = \frac{RT}{V_{H_3O^+} + V_{X^-}} \ln \frac{{}^{II}a_{H_3O^+}\,{}^{II}a_{X^-}}{{}^Ia_{H_3O^+}\,{}^Ia_{X^-}} \tag{7.63}$$

Elimination of $(p^I - p^{II})$ between Equations (7.60) and (7.63) gives

$$\frac{1}{V_{H_2O}} \ln \frac{{}^{II}a_{H_2O}}{{}^Ia_{H_2O}} = \frac{1}{V_{H_3O^+} + V_{X^-}} \ln \frac{{}^{II}a_\pm^2}{{}^Ia_\pm^2} \tag{7.64}$$

Or,

$$\frac{(^Ia_\pm)^2}{(^Ia_{H_2O})^x} = \frac{(^{II}a_\pm)^2}{(^{II}a_{H_2O})^x} \tag{7.65}$$

174

where

$$\frac{V_{H_2O^+} + V_{X^-}}{V_{H_2O}} = x$$

If $a_{H_2O} \sim 1$ in both phases, Equation (7.65) becomes

$$^{I}a_{\pm} \sim {}^{II}a_{\pm} \tag{7.66}$$

The expression for the membrane potential may be obtained by eliminating $(p^I - p^{II})$ between Equation (7.60) and either Equation (7.61) or (7.62). Thus,

$$\Delta\psi = \frac{RT}{F} \ln \frac{{}^{II}a_{H_3O^+}}{{}^{I}a_{H_3O^+}} \cdot \frac{({}^{I}a_{H_2O})^{x^+}}{({}^{II}a_{H_2O})^{x^+}} = \frac{RT}{F} \ln \frac{{}^{I}a_{X^-}}{{}^{II}a_{X^-}} \cdot \frac{({}^{II}a_{H_2O})^{x^-}}{({}^{I}a_{H_2O})^{x^-}} \tag{7.67}$$

where

$$x + = \frac{V_{H_3O^+}}{V_{H_2O}} \quad \text{and} \quad x - = \frac{V_{X^-}}{V_{H_2O}}$$

If again $^{I}a_{H_2O} \sim {}^{II}a_{H_2O}$

$$\Delta\psi \sim \frac{RT}{F} \ln \frac{{}^{II}a_{H_3O^+}}{{}^{I}a_{H_3O^+}} = \frac{RT}{F} \ln \frac{{}^{I}a_{X^-}}{{}^{II}a_{X^-}} \tag{7.68}$$

The general expression for the membrane potential is

$$\Delta\psi = \frac{RT}{nF} \ln \frac{{}^{II}a_i}{{}^{I}a_i} = \frac{RT}{F} \ln \lambda \tag{7.69}$$

Here λ is known as the *Donnan distribution coefficient*, expressed by the membrane equilibrium condition in the presence of various ion types by

$$\left(\frac{{}^{II}a_+}{{}^{I}a_+}\right) = \left(\frac{{}^{II}a_{2^+}}{{}^{I}a_{2^+}}\right)^{1/2} = \left(\frac{{}^{II}a_{3^+}}{{}^{I}a_{3^+}}\right)^{1/3} = \cdots$$

$$\cdots = \left(\frac{{}^{I}a_-}{{}^{II}a_-}\right) = \cdots \left(\frac{{}^{I}a_{3^-}}{{}^{II}a_{3^-}}\right)^{1/3} = \cdots = \lambda \tag{7.70}$$

Although the individual ion activities contained in λ cannot be measured, they may be replaced, for experimental purposes, by mean ion activities provided that solutions of such dilution are used that the Debye–Hückel limiting law holds.

The Donnan equilibrium is important in biological systems where it governs the movement of water and electrolytes into and out of cells. Chemical processes within the living cell can control the permeability of the cell membranes to various species.

7.8.1 Dialysis

Membrane equilibria are made use of in the separation by dialysis of inorganic ions from solutions of biologically important polyelectrolytes such as nucleic acids and proteins. Dialysis is based on the principle that a membrane allows free passage of small particles in true solution through it while retaining particles of colloidal dimensions. If the solvent on the exit side of the membrane is continuously renewed, the particles escaping through the membrane are removed, further transference through the membrane encouraged and separation of the colloid species feasible. In the technique of electrodialysis, removal of ions is made easier by an electric field. The solution containing the macro particles is placed between two membranes with pure solvent on either side and an e.m.f. imposed between electrodes placed in the solvent compartments.

It is sometimes advantageous to take advantage of membrane hydrolysis and this is used to convert proteins into acidic forms without recourse to conventional chemical means which might interfere with the system. Consider dialysis into pure water of a salt NaR from a solution through a membrane which allows passage of Na^+ but is impermeable to R^-

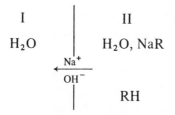

Sodium ions from II diffuse into I along with an equivalent number of hydroxyl ions. These latter arise from the dissociation of water which is necessary to maintain electroneutrality of I. The hydrogen ions produced by this process then associate with anions R^- to form the weak acid RH and maintain the electroneutrality of II. The initial and final equilibrium concentrations for the two solutions on either side of the membrane are as follows:

	I	II
Initial state	$[Na^+] = 0$	$[Na^+] = [R^-] = c$
Equilibrium condition	$[Na^+] = x = [OH^-]$	$[Na^+] = c - x$
		$[R^-] = c$
		$[H^+] = x$

At equilibrium we may write, in accordance with Equation (7.66)

$$(^I a_{Na^+} \cdot {^I a_{OH^-}}) = (^{II} a_{Na^+} \cdot {^{II} a_{OH^-}})$$

therefore,

$$x^2 \approx (c - x) \cdot \frac{K_W}{x}$$

therefore,

$$x = (K_W c)^{1/3} \qquad (7.71)$$

Although the number of sodium ions passing into I to meet the equilibrium conditions is not large, continuous replacement of solution I by pure water forces the process to continue by encouraging a continuous movement towards equilibrium. In this way the hydrolysis of the species NaR may be effected to a significant extent.

7.8.2   Ion-exchange resins

Typical cation exchange resins possess open three-dimensional structures with sulphonic acid groups attached in a regular manner throughout the network. For electroneutrality, there are required to be cations contained within the network (e.g., hydrogen or sodium ions) equal in number to the acid groups. If such a resin is placed in an acid or salt solution, water enters the free space in the network and causes swelling. We now have the situation where anions and cations of the dissolved species can move between the external solution and that inside the resin. The sulphonic acid groups, however, are fixed – not in this case by a membrane impermeable to their motion through it, but by chemical bonding. The effect will nevertheless be the same as for the membrane system. The solution inside the resin will show a larger osmotic pressure and the resin will continue to swell until a balance is achieved with the restoring forces of the extended structure. There will be an unequal distribution of electrolyte ions between the resin solution and the external solution.

In the case of a hydrogen ion-exchange resin placed in a solution of a 1 : 1 acid HA, while the ratio $[H^+]/[A^-]$ in the external solution must be 1 : 1, the ratio internally will be found to be up to several orders of magnitude greater than this. That is, the hydrogen ions are allowed ready access to the interior of the resin – in fact they pass almost unhindered through the resin with a transport number very close to unity – while the resin presents an almost impermeable barrier to the A^- anions. Anion-exchange resins work on the same principle with cathodic groups distributed through the interior network of the resin. Free passage of anions is now possible with almost total restriction on the entry and passage of cations through the resin.

Combinations of cation- and anion-exchange resins are used in electrolytic desalination plants to produce fresh water from brackish water or even sea water. The salt water is placed in a series of compartments separated alternately by anion and cation exchangers. A diagrammatic representation is given in Fig. 7.10. An e.m.f. applied between electrodes placed in the extreme cells constrains the ions to move in opposite directions through the solution in the field produced. Free movement is not possible, since it is restricted by the

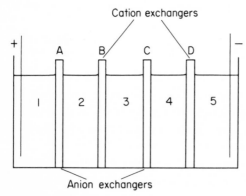

FIGURE 7.10
Schematic desalination plant.

ion exchangers. Thus the anion exchanger A allows free passage of anions from solution 2 to solution 1 but cations cannot pass from left to right through A to solution 2. Similarly, the cation exchanger B allows free passage of cations into solution 3 but does not allow anions through from 3 to 2. Thus, solution 1 becomes more concentrated in ions while solution 2 becomes more dilute. Similarly, solutions 3 and 5 become more concentrated and solution 4 more dilute. Such separation can continue until the desalination of solutions 2 and 4 is about 95% complete.

Further reading

Grahame, D. C. (1947), *Chemical Reviews,* **41,** 441, *Electrical Double Layer.*
Kryt, H. R. (1952), *Colloid Science*, Elsevier, Amsterdam.
Mohilner, D. M. (1966), *Electroanalytical Chemistry*, **1,** Ch. 4, *The Electrical Double Layer.*
Parsons, R. (1961), *Structure of Electrical Double Layer and its Influence on the Rates of Electrode Reactions*, in *Advances in Electrochemistry and Electrochemical Engineering*, Vol. 1, Interscience, New York.

Electrode processes 8

8.1 Non-equilibrium electrode potentials

In Chapter 5 we considered reversible potentials adopted by a metal electrode M, when placed in a solution of ions M^+. The steady potential resulted from the rapid establishment of the equilibrium

$$M \rightleftharpoons M^+ + e$$

no net current flowing when the forward and backward rates of the above system are equal. The further such an equilibrium lies to the right, the more negative is the electrode potential. If the equilibrium is established very rapidly, then it is possible for a potential rather more oxidizing or reducing than the equilibrium value to be imposed upon the electrode and to cause a net current flow but without unduly disturbing the electrode potential. This is because, although the applied excess potential causes a net reaction in one direction, the equilibrium re-asserts itself so rapidly that the electrode potential hardly alters, the Nernst equation still holding. A graph of current versus potential will ideally take the form shown in Fig. 8.1. The small slope is due to the relative slowness of mass transfer processes with respect to the electron exchange rate. If, however, such a large potential is applied that a large current flows the electrode equilibrium will not be able to maintain itself at a rate which can keep pace with that with which decomposition occurs. The potential must now alter if the current is to be maintained. The electrode process has now become effectively uni-directional and is said to take place irreversibly. The new potential will be more negative for a cathodic (reduction) process and more positive for an anodic (oxidation) process. The difference between an equilibrium and a non-equilibrium potential is known as over-

181

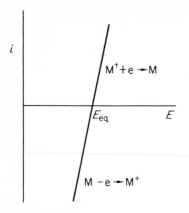

FIGURE 8.1
Ideal current–potential relationship for the system $M \rightleftharpoons M^+ + e$ in which equilibrium is established almost instantaneously.

voltage, normally given the symbol η. We have seen that some electrodes never show reversible potentials under normal experimental conditions because the rate of attainment of the electrode equilibrium is low – such processes are more realistically called *slow* rather than irreversible. In order for even a small cathodic or anodic current to flow, a potential well in excess of the equilibrium value must be applied to the respectively negative or posi-

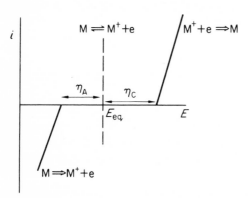

FIGURE 8.2
Current–potential relationship for a slow or irreversible system, requiring an overvoltage η_C for the process $M^+ + e \Rightarrow M$ and η_A for $M \Rightarrow M^+ + e$. In such cases the equilibrium condition $M \rightleftharpoons M^+ + e$ is not established and E_{eq} is hypothetical.

182

tive side of this value. For such cases a current–voltage curve will take the form shown in Fig. 8.2. Here, the cathodic and anodic overvoltages are labelled η_C and η_A and they represent the minimum values which will show a net current for a cathodic or anodic reaction.

8.2   Electrode kinetics

For the process

$$Ox + ne \underset{k_{-1}}{\overset{k_1}{\rightleftharpoons}} Red$$

in which k_1 and k_{-1} are the formal rate constants of the forward and backward reactions as written, we may write the forward and backward rates, r_1 and r_{-1} as

$$r_1 = k_1[Ox]_e; \qquad r_{-1} = k_{-1}[Red]_e$$

the subscripts e referring to concentrations at the electrode surface – which for the present purposes may be regarded as the edge of the diffuse double layer (see Fig. 8.3). Since the mathematical treatment is considerably com-

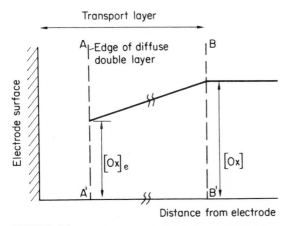

FIGURE 8.3

Concentration variations in the vicinity of an electrode. When Ox undergoes reduction, its concentration at A–A' becomes depleted and a concentration gradient is set up between A–A' and the bulk B–B'. Across the transport layer thus formed, mass transfer takes place.

183

plicated by taking double layer effects into account, we shall simplify our arguments by considering $[Ox]_e$ and $[Red]_e$ as concentrations of oxidized and reduced forms very near to the electrode surface, but just outside the boundary of the diffuse layer.

The forward and backward rates may be expressed in terms of the forward (cathodic) and backward (anodic) current densities, I_1 and I_{-1}, thus

$$r_1 = \frac{I_1}{nF} = k_1[Ox]_e \tag{8.1}$$

and

$$r_{-1} = \frac{I_{-1}}{nF} = k_{-1}[Red]_e \tag{8.2}$$

Consider the case that $r_1 > r_{-1}$, i.e. if Ox refers to a metal ion and Red to the metal itself, discharge occurs more rapidly than dissolution. The process is irreversible and the potential departs from the reversible value by $\eta = (E - E^\ominus)$. The effect of η is twofold: part of it makes the discharge process more rapid (a net cathodic current is observed) and part of it retards the dissolution process. This occurs by a decrease of the activation energy barrier to the forward process and an increase of the barrier to the backward reaction (Fig. 8.4).

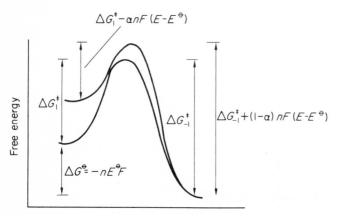

Distance from electrode surface

FIGURE 8.4
Effect of overvoltage, $(E - E^\ominus)$, upon free energy profile of an electrode reaction.

Thus, if α is the fraction of the overpotential assisting discharge, the activation energy, $\Delta G_1^{\ddagger}$, which would be required if the process were to occur reversibly is reduced to $(\Delta G_1^{\ddagger} - \alpha nF(E - E^{\ominus}))$. Similarly, the activation energy, $\Delta G_{-1}^{\ddagger}$, is increased to $(\Delta G_{-1}^{\ddagger} + (1 - \alpha)nF(E - E^{\ominus}))$. We may therefore express the forward and backward rates in the form

$$r_1 = k_1' \,[Ox]_e \exp\left[\frac{-\Delta G_1^{\ddagger} - \alpha nF(E - E^{\ominus})}{RT}\right] \qquad (8.3)$$

and

$$r_{-1} = k_{-1}' \,[Red]_e \exp\left[\frac{-\Delta G_{-1}^{\ddagger} + (1 - \alpha)nF(E - E^{\ominus})}{RT}\right] \qquad (8.4)$$

Alternatively,

$$r_1 = k_1{}^0[Ox]_e \exp\left[\frac{-\alpha nFE}{RT}\right] \qquad (8.5)$$

and

$$r_{-1} = k_{-1}{}^0[Red]_e \exp\left[\frac{(1 - \alpha)nFE}{RT}\right] \qquad (8.6)$$

Here, $k_1{}^0$ and $k_{-1}{}^0$ are potential independent constants characteristic of the two reactions.

A comparison of Equations (8.1) and (8.2) with (8.5) and (8.6) shows that the formal rate constants k_1, k_{-1} are dependent upon potential:

$$k_1 = k_1{}^0 \exp\left[\frac{-\alpha nFE}{RT}\right] \qquad (8.7)$$

and

$$k_{-1} = k_{-1}{}^0 \exp\left[\frac{(1 - \alpha)nFE}{RT}\right] \qquad (8.8)$$

At the standard electrode potential, $E^{\ominus}$, $k_1 = k_{-1} = k^0$, the *standard electrode reaction rate constant*. Therefore,

$$k^0 = k_1{}^0 \exp\left[\frac{-\alpha nFE^{\ominus}}{RT}\right] \qquad (8.9)$$

$$= k_{-1}{}^0 \exp\left[\frac{(1 - \alpha)nFE^{\ominus}}{RT}\right] \qquad (8.10)$$

Thus, the forward and backward rates may each be expressed in terms of a single rate constant k^0, if the electrode potential is measured with respect to $E^{\ominus}$. Alternative expressions for the two rates are thus

$$r_1 = k^0 [Ox]_e \exp \left[\frac{-\alpha nF (E - E^{\ominus})}{RT} \right] \qquad (8.11)$$

and

$$r_{-1} = k^0 [Red]_e \exp \left[\frac{(1 - \alpha)nF(E - E^{\ominus})}{RT} \right] \qquad (8.12)$$

Further, the current densities for the two processes are given by Equations (8.1) and (8.2) as

$$I_1 = nFk^0 [Ox]_e \exp \left[\frac{-\alpha nF(E - E^{\ominus})}{RT} \right] \qquad (8.13)$$

and

$$I_{-1} = -nFk^0 [Red]_e \exp \left[\frac{(1 - \alpha)nF(E - E^{\ominus})}{RT} \right] \qquad (8.14)$$

Now, the net current density,

$$I = I_1 + I_{-1} \qquad (8.15)$$

i.e.,

$$I = nFk^0 \left\{ [Ox]_e \exp \left[\frac{-\alpha nF(E - E^{\ominus})}{RT} \right] \right.$$
$$\left. - [Red]_e \exp \left[\frac{(1 - \alpha)nF(E - E^{\ominus})}{RT} \right] \right\} \qquad (8.16)$$

It is seen from a comparison of Equation (8.16) with Equations (8.1) and (8.2) that the formal rate constants are now given by

$$k_1 = k^0 \exp \left[\frac{-\alpha nF(E - E^{\ominus})}{RT} \right] \qquad (8.17)$$

and

$$k_{-1} = k^0 \exp \left[\frac{(1 - \alpha)nF(E - E^{\ominus})}{RT} \right] \qquad (8.18)$$

From Equations (8.9) and (8.10) we see that

$$\frac{k_1{}^0}{k_{-1}{}^0} = \exp\left[\frac{nFE^\ominus}{RT}\right] \qquad (8.19)$$

i.e.

$$E^\ominus = \frac{RT}{nF} \ln \frac{k_1{}^0}{k_{-1}{}^0} \qquad (8.20)$$

Now, at *any equilibrium potential*, E_e, the *net* current density is zero, the exchange current density, I_0, flowing equally in both directions. Since the net current is zero, there is zero concentration gradient at the electrode surface, i.e., $[Ox]_e = [Ox]$ and $[Red]_e = [Red]$ if $E = E_e$. Therefore,

$$I_1 = I_{-1} = I_0$$

$$= nFk_1{}^0[Ox] \exp\left[\frac{-\alpha nFE_e}{RT}\right]$$

$$= nFk_{-1}{}^0[Red] \exp\left[\frac{(1-\alpha)nFE_e}{RT}\right] \qquad (8.21)$$

and

$$\frac{k_1{}^0[Ox]}{k_{-1}{}^0[Red]} = \exp\left[\frac{nFE_e}{RT}\right]$$

or

$$E_e = \frac{RT}{nF} \ln\left[\frac{k_1{}^0[Ox]}{k_{-1}{}^0[Red]}\right] = \frac{RT}{nF} \ln \frac{k_1{}^0}{k_{-1}{}^0} + \frac{RT}{nF} \ln \frac{[Ox]}{[Red]} \qquad (8.22)$$

or

$$E_e = E^\ominus + \frac{RT}{nF} \ln \frac{[Ox]}{[Red]} \qquad (8.23)$$

Equation (8.23) is the Nernst equation which previously was derived thermodynamically. Equation (8.20) may further be expressed as

$$\frac{nFE^\ominus}{RT} = \ln \frac{k_1{}^0}{k_{-1}{}^0}$$

Or, multiplying through by $(1 - \alpha)$

$$(1 - \alpha) \frac{nFE^{\ominus}}{RT} = (1 - \alpha) \ln \frac{k_1{}^0}{k_{-1}{}^0}$$

$$= \ln \frac{k^0}{k_{-1}{}^0} \qquad \text{(from Equation (8.10))}$$

Therefore,

$$k^0 = k_1^0 \left(\frac{k_1{}^0}{k_{-1}{}^0} \right)^{1-\alpha} = (k_1{}^0)^{(1-\alpha)}(k_{-1}{}^0)^{\alpha} \qquad (8.24)$$

From Equation (8.21)

$$I_0 = nF\dot{k}_{-1}{}^0 [\text{Red}] \exp \left[\frac{(1 - \alpha)nFE_e}{RT} \right]$$

$$= nFk_{-1}{}^0 [\text{Red}] \exp \left[(1 - \alpha) \ln \left(\frac{k_1{}^0 [\text{Ox}]}{k_{-1}{}^0 [\text{Red}]} \right) \right] \qquad (8.25)$$

by substituting for nFE_e/RT from the Nernst equation. Therefore,

$$I_0 = nFk_{-1}{}^0 [\text{Red}] \left(\frac{k_1{}^0 [\text{Ox}]}{k_{-1}{}^0 [\text{Red}]} \right)^{1-\alpha}$$

$$= nF(k_{-1}{}^0)^{\alpha}(k_1{}^0)^{1-\alpha}([\text{Ox}])^{1-\alpha}([\text{Red}])^{\alpha}$$

or

$$I_0 = nFk^0([\text{Ox}])^{1-\alpha}([\text{Red}])^{\alpha} \qquad (8.26)$$

by substitution from Equation (8.24).

Thus the exchange current density is a function of both [Ox] and [Red] and does not uniquely describe the rate of reaction, unlike k^0. At $E = E^{\ominus}$, [Ox] = [Red] and Equation (8.26) becomes

$$I_0{}^0 = nFk^0 \qquad (8.27)$$

$I_0{}^0$ being the *standard exchange current density.*

We are now in a position to express the current density at a potential E in terms of the exchange current density at *any equilibrium potential, E_e.* The net current density at applied potential E is given by

$$I = nFk_1^0[\text{Ox}] \exp\left[\frac{-\alpha nFE}{RT}\right] - nFk_{-1}^0[\text{Red}] \exp\left[\frac{(1 - \alpha)nFE}{RT}\right]$$

$$(8.28)$$

and dividing Equation (8.28) by Equation (8.21) we obtain

$$I = I_0 \left\{\exp\left[\frac{-\alpha nF\eta}{RT}\right] - \exp\left[\frac{(1 - \alpha)nF\eta}{RT}\right]\right\} \qquad (8.29)$$

where $(E - E_e) = \eta$ the overvoltage.

8.3   Dependence of current density on overvoltage. The Tafel equation

If the overvoltage is small the exponential terms of Equation (8.29) may be expanded and all terms except the first two neglected. The expression then simplifies to

$$I = \frac{I_0 nF\eta}{RT} \qquad (8.30)$$

For higher overvoltages the full expression (8.29) must be used. In Fig. 8.5 calculated values of the ratio I/I_0 are plotted as a function of overvoltage for $\alpha = 0\cdot5$, the I_c, I_a curves are the partial exchange current density ratios. Figure 8.6 shows two further similar plots for a transfer coefficient of $0\cdot25$ and $0\cdot75$. It is seen that for all cases, $I/I_0 = 0$ when $\eta = 0$.

For a large overvoltage to the cathodic reaction, only the first exponential term in Equation (8.29) is significant, the second being very small by comparison. The dependence of net cathodic current on overvoltage may then be given by

$$\log I = -\frac{\alpha nF\eta}{RT} \log I_0$$

or

$$\eta = \frac{2\cdot303RT}{\alpha nF} \log I_0 - \frac{2\cdot303RT}{\alpha nF} \log I \qquad (8.31)$$

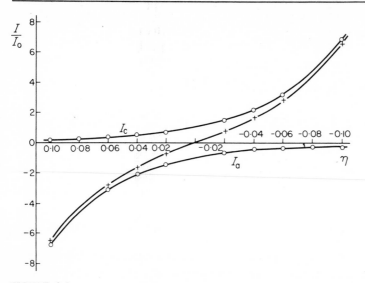

FIGURE 8.5
The ratio I/I_0 (calculated from Equation (8.29)) plotted as a function of overvoltage, η. I_c, I_a are the partial cathodic and anodic current density ratios. $\alpha = 0.5$.

Conversely, for a large overvoltage to the anodic reaction, only the second exponential term of Equation (8.29) is important and, by analogy with Equation (8.31), we may write

$$\eta = -\frac{2 \cdot 303RT}{(1 - \alpha)nF} \log I_0 + \frac{2 \cdot 303RT}{(1 - \alpha)nF} \log I \qquad (8.32)$$

Equations (8.31) and (8.32) are of identical form to an empirical equation put forward by Tafel as

$$\eta = a + b \log I \qquad (8.33)$$

Graphs of η versus $\log I$ are known as Tafel plots, and examples are shown in Fig. 8.7.

The linear portions of the asymptotes correspond to the Tafel equation and have slopes (Tafel slopes) of magnitude b; $2 \cdot 303RT/\alpha nF$ for the cathodic and $2 \cdot 303RT/(1 - \alpha)nF$ for the anodic process. An experimental line does not continue and cut the $\log I$ axis, since I refers to a *net* current density. This will approach zero as η approaches zero. The extrapolated asymptotes intersect on the line $\eta = 0$ at $\log I_0$.

190

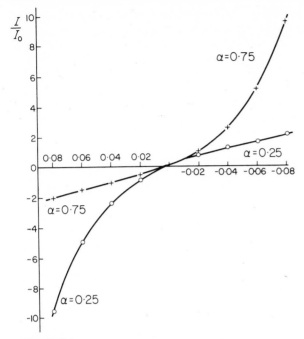

FIGURE 8.6
The ratio I/I_0 (calculated from Equation (8.29)) plotted as a function of overvoltage, η, for $\alpha = 0.25$ and 0.75.

It is apparent that I_0 is very small for an irreversible process, since if no overvoltage is applied I_0 is given by an equation of the form

$$I_0 = k\, e^{-\Delta G^{\ddagger}/RT} \tag{8.34}$$

so that for large $\Delta G^{\ddagger}$, I_0 is very small. The ratio I/I_0 from Equation (8.29) is large (even for small I) and the values of the two exponential terms differ considerably. On the other hand, when I_0 is large, as for a reversible process, the ratio I/I_0 is always extremely small and the two exponential terms are very nearly equal, corresponding to Nernstian conditions. The Nernst equation will hold when a small net current flows in such cases, provided that I is very much smaller than I_0. The magnitude of I_0 for a given process will determine the deviation of the electrode potential from its equilibrium value when an external current is caused to flow. The larger the deviation, the slower is the electrode reaction.

191

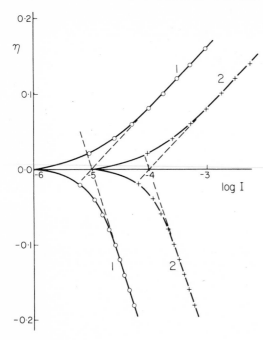

FIGURE 8.7.
Tafel plots constructed using data from Fig. 8.6.

1. $\alpha = 0.25; I_0 = 10^{-5}$.
2. $\alpha = 0.25; I_0 = 10^{-4}$.

8.4 Electrolysis and overvoltage

It is necessary to consider a number of types of overvoltage, their source and control and the way in which they influence the course of an electrochemical reaction.

8.4.1 Activation overvoltage

A slow electron transfer, such as that considered in the previous section, has a high activation energy. If such a reaction is to proceed at a reasonable rate and produce an efficient quantity of product, a significant increase of applied potential over the equilibrium value is necessary. This excess potential is

192

known as *activation overvoltage.* This description emphasizes that the slow, rate-determining step in the process is the electron transfer due to the high activation energy barrier which it must cross.

Two further types of overvoltage are of importance and may occur simultaneously with activation overvoltage.

8.4.2 Resistance overvoltage

The most common form of resistance overvoltage arises from the passage of electric current through an electrolyte solution surrounding the electrode. Such a solution is not of infinite conductivity and shows resistance to the current flow, with the result that an ohmic (iR) drop in potential occurs between the working electrodes. This effect may be offset by insulating the solution of the reference electrode from the working solution by enclosing the former in a fine glass capillary, the open end of which is brought as close to the surface of the electrode under investigation as is compatible with a uniform field force over the surface of this electrode (Fig. 8.8).

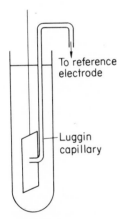

FIGURE 8.8
The Luggin capillary (schematic).

The optimum position of this Luggin capillary, as it is called, is usually a matter of experiment.

A less common form of ohmic overvoltage is caused by the formation, on the surface of the electrode, of an adherent layer of reaction product which is a relatively poor conductor of electricity. Surface oxide films show such behaviour, their resistance being such that overvoltages of several hundred volts may be produced.

8.4.3 Concentration overvoltage

This is a small, but important, effect which arises due to concentration changes induced in the vicinity of electrodes by electrochemical reactions occurring there.

Consider the simplest of all possible electrolysis cells in which two identical electrodes, M, dip into a solution of M^+ ions and let the electrode equilibria be established rapidly, i.e. if no external potential is applied, but the cell is simply short-circuited, no current will flow since the potential of both electrodes is the same.

If even a small potential difference is applied between the electrodes, the balance is destroyed, one electrode becoming a cathode the other an anode. At the former M^+ ions are discharged at a faster rate than they dissolve and at the anode M passes into solution more rapidly than M^+ ions are discharged.

The total amount of material discharged at the cathode or dissolved from the anode may be calculated from Faraday's laws, from a knowledge of the quantity of electricity passed. However, by reference to the Hittorf mechanism of electrolysis, we see that, at the cathode, only a fraction t_+ of the material deposited there has reached there by electrical migration. The remaining fraction must be made good from the layer of solution in the immediate vicinity of the electrode surface. From the moment that electrolysis starts, therefore, the solution close to the cathode surface shows a concentration decrease. For the same current to flow, and therefore the same rate of deposition of M^+, a more negative potential will be required. Similarly, a more positive potential will be required at the anode since here only a fraction t_+ of the metal ions formed by dissolution are removed by migration so that the concentration of the anode solution increases. The effect is to produce a back e.m.f., so that to maintain the current flow, the applied e.m.f. must be increased by this amount. An electrode whose potential deviates from its equilibrium value due to these causes is said to be 'concentration polarized'. Stirring of the electrolyte solution or rotation or vibration of the electrodes can serve to reduce the extent of concentration polarization but does not eliminate it entirely.

At an electrode surface there is a diffusion layer across which there is a concentration variation from the surface to the edge of the layer. To a good approximation this variation may be regarded as uniformly linear (Fig. 8.9).

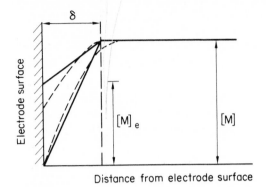

FIGURE 8.9
Schematic representation of the concentration gradient in the vicinity of an electrode at which reduction is occurring.

The thickness of the layer, δ, has a magnitude of the order of 0·05 cm under static conditions, which becomes reduced to the region of 0·001 cm with rapid stirring.

For a steady current through the cell, the concentration of the surface-layer of solution at the cathode falls and is made good by the diffusion of material from the bulk. A steady state is rapidly reached where M^+ ions removed by deposition are replaced by those arriving by both electrical migration and diffusion. The rate of arrival of M^+ ions by diffusion in mole cm^{-2} s^{-1} is given by

$$\frac{D([M] - [M]_e)}{\delta} \qquad (8.35)$$

D being the diffusion coefficient of the species M^+, and is defined as the amount of M^+ transported per unit area across unit diffusion layer thickness under unit concentration gradient in unit time.

The rate of arrival at the cathode of M^+ ions by migration is, for a current density I,

$$\frac{t_+ I}{nF} \qquad (8.36)$$

195

Since the total amount deposited is given by I/nF, it follows that, under steady state conditions,

$$\frac{I}{nF} = \frac{t_+I}{nF} + \frac{D([M] - [M]_e)}{\delta} \qquad (8.37)$$

As the potential impressed between the electrodes is increased, the current density will increase so long as the concentration gradient across the diffusion layer can increase to maintain the supply of M^+. A point will, however, be reached where $[M]_e$ becomes zero. Since the concentration gradient has now reached its maximum value, the rate of supply of M^+ by diffusion has reached its maximum value and the electrode process can proceed no faster. Equation (8.37) now becomes

$$\frac{I_{lim}}{nF} = \frac{t_+I_{lim}}{nF} + \frac{D[M]}{\delta} \qquad (8.38)$$

Comparing Equations (8.37) and (8.38) we see that

$$\frac{I(1 - t_+)/nF}{I_{lim}(1 - t_+)/nF} = \frac{([M] - [M]_e)}{[M]} \qquad (8.39)$$

or,

$$\frac{[M]}{[M]_e} = \frac{I_{lim}}{I_{lim} - I} \qquad (8.40)$$

So that the concentration overvoltage, ΔE, may be written

$$\Delta E = \frac{RT}{nF} \ln \frac{[M]}{[M]_e} = \frac{RT}{nF} \ln \frac{I_{lim}}{I_{lim} - I} \qquad (8.41)$$

8.4.4 *Summary of overvoltage phenomena and their distinguishing features*

The overvoltage of an individual electrode may be expressed as the sum of contributions from activation, concentration and resistive film overvoltages

$$\eta = \eta_A + \eta_C + \eta_R \qquad (8.42)$$

the use of the Luggin capillary virtually eliminating the iR contribution. Hence, η_R is often absent.

There are a number of distinguishing features of the above three forms of overvoltage which allow the effects to be identified experimentally.

(a) η_R, unlike η_A and η_C, appears and disappears instantaneously when the polarizing circuit is made or broken.

(b) η_A increases rapidly and exponentially after a polarizing current is caused to flow and decreases in a complementary way when the current flow is stopped. The exponential growth and decay are in accordance with the concept of η_A as a function of the activation energy of an electrode process. The magnitude of η_A is strongly affected by the physical and chemical nature of the electrode material.

(c) η_C grows and decays slowly on application or interruption of the current flow at a rate characteristic of the diffusion coefficients of the species involved. η_C is unique in being the only form of overvoltage affected by stirring and is unaffected by the nature of the surface of the electrode material.

8.5   Hydrogen and oxygen overvoltage

The evolution of hydrogen and oxygen are well-known phenomena during electrolysis of dilute aqueous solutions of acids and bases between inert metal electrodes. If bright platinum electrodes are used for the electrolysis, it is found that in most cases the minimum potential difference which must be applied between them before gas bubbles appear is close to 1·7 V. That a similar value should usually be observed is hardly surprising since the same overall chemical process is occurring, viz. the decomposition of water.

8.5.1   Decomposition potentials and overvoltage

A graph of current, or current density, versus potential gives a decomposition curve and allows decomposition potentials to be determined (Fig. 8.10). Decomposition potentials are never well-defined and can only be obtained approximately by extrapolation of the rising part of the curve to the potential axis. Nevertheless the value of approximately 1·7 V for the electrolysis of water is sufficiently different from the theoretical value for it to be apparent that there is a large cell overvoltage even when resistance and concentration

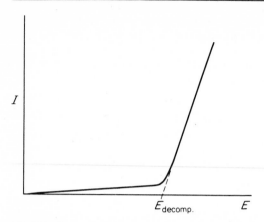

FIGURE 8.10

Decomposition curve. E_{decomp} is the minimum potential difference which must be applied between a pair of electrodes before decomposition occurs and a current flows. E_{decomp} has little theoretical significance since it is made up of two individual electrode potentials and their associated overvoltages.

effects are taken account of. The theoretical decomposition potential may be calculated as follows: the reaction occurring in the electrolysis cell is

$$H_2O(l) \rightarrow H_2(g) + \tfrac{1}{2} O_2(g)$$

for which $\Delta G^{\ominus} \sim 238\ 140$ joules. Now $\Delta G^{\ominus} = -nFE^{\ominus}$ where, for the present case $E^{\ominus}$ is the standard e.m.f. of the hydrogen–oxygen cell; therefore,

$$E^{\ominus} = -\frac{238\ 140}{2 \times 96\ 500} = -1 \cdot 23\ V$$

The cell overvoltage observed when using bright platinum electrodes is thus of the order of 0·5 V. An experimental decomposition voltage *has no theoretical significance* of its own, since a moment's consideration will show that it consists of *two* individual electrode potentials and the iR drop between them. These individual potentials will be made up of the thermodynamic values plus the overvoltages; the latter comprising contributions from activation, concentration and film resistance overvoltage.

8.5.2 *Individual electrode overvoltages*

Individual electrode overvoltages may be determined experimentally by measuring the potential of the individual electrodes at a given current den-

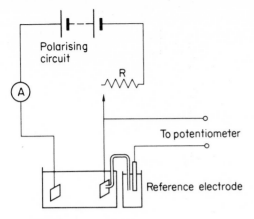

FIGURE 8.11
Determination of individual electrode overvoltages and elimination of *iR* contribution.

sity. The circuit required is shown in Fig. 8.11. Here a constant electrolysis current density is maintained by a high-tension battery/series resistance combination to polarize the electrodes. Each electrode in turn is then combined with a reference electrode and the e.m.f.'s of the two cells successively formed in this way measured via the potentiometer. Since the reference electrode potential is known, the potential of the anode and cathode may be determined at the current density imposed. The Luggin capillary, brought as close to the electrode surfaces as possible, largely removes the *iR* contribution to the measured overpotential. By these means the *cell* overvoltage of about 0·5 V for the above case may be shown to comprise an overvoltage of about 0·1 V

TABLE 8.1
Selected hydrogen overvoltages for various electrode materials in dilute sulphuric acid

Metal	η (V)
Hg	0·78
Zn	0·70
Sn	0·53
Cu	0·23
Ni	0·21
Pt (bright)	0·10
Pt (platinized)	0·005

at the cathode and about 0·4 V at the anode. In Table 8.1 are collected approximate hydrogen overvoltages for various electrode materials in dilute sulphuric acid.

8.6   Some theories of hydrogen overvoltage

The essential stages in the overall process of hydrogen discharge and gas evolution at a cathode may be assumed to be as follows:

(1) H_3O^+ ions diffuse from the bulk solution to the edge of the double layer.
(2) H_3O^+ ions are transferred across the layer.
(3) Dehydration of H_3O^+.
(4) H^+ receives an electron from the electrode.
        Stages (2), (3) and (4) constitute the discharge reaction which we may express as

$$M + H_3O^+ + e \rightarrow M\text{---}H + H_2O \qquad (8.43)$$
(H atom adsorbed onto electrode surface)

(5) Formation of hydrogen molecules from hydrogen atoms. This can occur in one of two possible ways, viz.

$$\text{(i)} \qquad M\text{---}H + M\text{---}H \rightarrow 2M + H_2 \qquad (8.44)$$
(often called the catalytic reaction)

$$\text{or, (ii)} \quad M\text{---}H + H_3O^+ + e \rightarrow M + H_2 + H_2O \qquad (8.45)$$
(i.e. a new H_3O^+ ion interacts on the electrode surface – this is often called the electrochemical reaction).

(6) Desorption of hydrogen molecules.
(7) Formation of bubbles and evolution of gas.

The problem is to decide which stages are rate-determining. If stage (1) were to be rate-determining, then the process overall would be diffusion-limited due to concentration polarization. Usually, one of the stages (2) to (5) is the slowest. Which one, depends upon many factors such as the operating conditions and the nature of the cathode.

8.6.1 The catalytic theory

Tafel proposed that (5)(i) of the above scheme was the slow stage. Since the standard potential of a hydrogen electrode is zero, by definition, its potential, under conditions other than standard may be given by

$$E = \frac{RT}{F} \ln \frac{a_{H^+}}{a_{H_2}^{1/2}} \tag{8.46}$$

$$= \frac{2 \cdot 303 RT}{F} \log a_{H^+} - \frac{2 \cdot 303 RT}{2F} \log p_{H_2} \tag{8.47}$$

assuming that the activity of the gas may be equated to its partial pressure. Equation (8.47) may be further expressed in terms of hydrogen atoms formed since

$$2H \underset{}{\overset{K_p}{\rightleftharpoons}} H_2; \quad p_{H_2} = K_p p_H^2 \tag{8.48}$$

so that Equation (8.47) becomes

$$E = K - \frac{2 \cdot 303 RT}{2F} \log p_H^2 \tag{8.49}$$

where K is a further constant.

The rate of formation of hydrogen molecules is given by

$$-\frac{d[H]}{dt} = k p_H^2 = f(I) \tag{8.50}$$

k being the appropriate specific rate. This rate is a function of the current density so that

$$I = k' p_H^2$$

or,

$$\log I = \log k' + \log p_H^2 \tag{8.51}$$

and further,

$$E = K' - \frac{2 \cdot 303 RT}{2F} \log I \tag{8.52}$$

k' and K' being further constants.

Equation (8.52) is of the form of the Tafel equation (8.33) which suggests that b is approximately $0 \cdot 03$. Such a value is rarely encountered in practice although it is observed in the case of platinized platinum. The above treatment does not allow for the fact that the pH of the solution will be modified by the adsorption process, relative concentrations of free and adsorbed atoms being given by the Freundlich isotherm

$$[H_{ads}] = k p_H^{1/n} \tag{8.53}$$

Inclusion of this restriction requires modification of Equation (8.52) to the following

$$E = K' - \frac{2 \cdot 303 nRT}{2F} \log I \tag{8.54}$$

8.6.2 The slow discharge theory

A further theory of hydrogen overvoltage regards the overall stage (2) to (4) of the scheme as rate-determining, i.e. the discharge reaction. If the modern view of the double layer is assumed, in that part of the potential difference occurs in the diffuse part of the layer and does not contribute to charge transfer across the Helmholtz layer, the effective potential difference to be considered is $(\psi - \zeta)$, as described in Chapter 7. The rate of discharge may then be given in the form

$$I = (k a_{H_3O^+} e^{\zeta F/RT}) e^{\alpha(\psi - \zeta)F/RT} \tag{8.55}$$

It is seen that the second exponential term is of the same *form* as that used previously, i.e. the electrochemical form of the Arrhenius equation. The first exponential term expresses the influence of the diffuse double layer on the rate by virtue of its effect upon the number of H_3O^+ ions available for reduction. If α is taken as having a value of approximately $0 \cdot 5$, then

$$I = (k a_{H_3O^+} e^{\zeta F/RT})(e^{(\psi - \zeta)F/2RT})$$

and

$$I = (k a_{H_3O^+} e^{\zeta F/2RT})(e^{\psi F/2RT}) \tag{8.56}$$

Now ψ of double layer theory corresponds to E so that, taking logarithms, we have

$$\ln \frac{I}{ka_{H_3O^+}} = \frac{\zeta F}{2RT} + \frac{EF}{2RT} = \frac{F}{2RT}(\zeta + E) \tag{8.57}$$

or,

$$(E + \zeta) = \frac{2RT}{F} \ln I - \frac{2RT}{F} \ln a_{H_3O^+} + \text{constant} \tag{8.58}$$

Now, the reversible hydrogen potential is given by

$$E_R = \frac{RT}{F} \ln a_{H_3O^+} \tag{8.59}$$

Substitution of Equation (8.59) and the relation $\eta = (E - E_R)$ into Equation (8.58) yields

$$\zeta + \eta = \frac{2RT}{F} \ln I - \frac{RT}{F} \ln a_{H_3O^+} + \text{constant} \tag{8.60}$$

therefore,

$$\eta = \text{constant} + \frac{2 \times 2.303RT}{F} \log I = \text{constant} + b \log I \tag{8.61}$$

in which $b = 0.118$ at 298 K. This value of b is observed for many of the higher overvoltage metals. The validity of the slow discharge theory is further supported by the observed linear correlation between values of overvoltage and those of adsorption energy for a range of metals. For a particularly high value of adsorption energy, it is clear that the discharge reaction will have quite a small activation energy. This might well mean that this process takes place so readily that some other step in the scheme may become rate-determining.

A value of 0.5 for α seems to have general validity for such mechanisms. At one time this value tended to be given to it because there was none other available, but a consideration of the *Electrostatic Interaction Energy* between charges in an electrical double layer, gives this energy the value

$$\tfrac{1}{2} \times \text{charge} \times \text{potential difference}$$

So that the electrostatic interaction energy, for an overvoltage η, is $\eta F/2RT$ and it is by this amount that the activation energy of an electrode reaction is considered to be reduced.

8.6.3 The electrochemical theory

This theory considers reaction 5(ii) of the scheme to control the rate. For this reaction to take place, hydrogen atoms must already be in strategic positions on the electrode surface so that it is necessary to consider essentially three processes as follows

$$M + H_3O^+ + e \underset{k_2}{\overset{k_1}{\rightleftharpoons}} M{-}H$$

$$M{-}H + H_3O^+ + e \xrightarrow{k_3} H_2 + M + H_2O$$

Since the protons must be dehydrated, these may be considered as

$$H^+ + e \xrightarrow{k_1} H \text{ (adsorbed)} \qquad \text{(i)}$$

$$H \text{ (adsorbed)} \xrightarrow{k_2} H^+ + e \qquad \text{(ii)}$$

and

$$H \text{ (adsorbed)} + H^+ + e \xrightarrow{k_3} H_2 \qquad \text{(iii)}$$

If these three stages require activation energies $\Delta G_1^\ddagger$, $\Delta G_2^\ddagger$ and $\Delta G_3^\ddagger$ respectively, and if $\alpha = 0.5$ in each case for an overvoltage η, then the individual rates may be given by

$$r_1 = k_1[H^+]\, e^{-(\Delta G_1^\ddagger - \frac{1}{2}\eta F)/RT} \qquad (8.62)$$

$$r_2 = k_2[H]\, e^{-(\Delta G_2^\ddagger + \frac{1}{2}\eta F)/RT} \qquad (8.63)$$

(this reaction is the reverse of (i) and, by definition, α is the fraction of applied potential *hindering* this process), and

$$r_3 = k_3[H][H^+]\, e^{-(\Delta G_3^\ddagger - \frac{1}{2}\eta F)/RT} \qquad (8.64)$$

For a stationary state, corresponding to a uniform rate of hydrogen evolution, $[H] = $ constant and

$$k_1'[H^+]\, e^{\eta F/2RT} - k_2'[H]\, e^{-\eta F/2RT} - k_3'[H][H^+]\, e^{\eta F/2RT} = 0 \qquad (8.65)$$

Here, the terms $e^{-\Delta G^{\ddagger}/RT}$ have been combined with the respective k's. Therefore,

$$[H]_{\text{absorbed}} = \frac{k_1'[H^+]\, e^{\eta F/2RT}}{k_2'\, e^{-\eta F/2RT} + k_3'[H^+]\, e^{\eta F/RT}} \qquad (8.66)$$

This may now be substituted into Equation (8.64) to give

$$r_3 = \frac{k_1' k_3'[H^+]^2\, e^{\eta F/RT}}{k_2'\, e^{-\eta F/2RT} + k_3'\,[H^+] e^{\eta F/2RT}} \qquad (8.67)$$

It is unlikely that the denominator terms will be comparable, so that, if the term in k_2' is relatively unimportant compared with that in k_3',

$$r_3 = k_1'[H^+]\, e^{\eta F/2RT} \qquad (8.68)$$

This last equation is again seen to be a form of the Tafel equation with the constant $b = 0.118$ at 298 K. Since it only holds for small k_2, this implies a small exchange current and a metal which is not a very efficient hydrogenation catalyst.

If the second term in the denominator of Equation (8.67) is negligible compared to the first, the rate becomes

$$r_3 = \frac{k_1' k_3'}{k_2'}\, [H^+]^2\, e^{3\eta F/2RT} \qquad (8.69)$$

This is once again of the Tafel form, but with $b = 0.04$ at 298 K.

It is clear that no one theory can account for all classes of behaviour under all conditions. For low overvoltage metals, it seems probable that the catalytic process is rate-determining, while for metals showing higher overvoltages, slow ion discharge theories are more successful in explaining observed behaviour. In a smaller number of instances, the electrochemical theory is more successful, for example in explaining the behaviour of silver and nickel in alkaline solution where η is observed to be a function of the pH of the solution as required by the equations above.

For electrode materials with high catalytic activity, it would appear that the slow stage in the hydrogen evolution process can be the removal of molecular hydrogen from the electrode surface by diffusion.

8.7   Polarography

Polarography is an electrochemical technique which makes use of current–voltage curves under conditions of concentration polarization of an indicator electrode. Equation (8.37) gave the total rate of deposition of a metal ion M^+ in terms of the rates of the two mass transfer processes, migration and diffusion viz.

$$\frac{I}{nF} = \frac{t_+ I}{nF} + \frac{D([M] - [M]_e)}{\delta} \qquad \text{(see Equation (8.37))}$$

or

$$\frac{I_{\text{lim}}}{nF} = \frac{t_+ I_{\text{lim}}}{nF} + \frac{D[M]}{\delta} \qquad \text{(see Equation (8.38))}$$

when the diffusion rate is at a maximum, corresponding to zero surface concentration of the cation.

Equation (8.38) relates the limiting current density to the concentration of the species M^+. Unfortunately, it also involves the transport number, t_+, of this species and since this quantity varies with conditions and concentration, Equation (8.38) could not, as it stands, hold very promising analytical possibilities. However, there is a very simple way of almost completely eliminating the electrical migration effect. We have seen in an earlier chapter that t_+ for a given ion is diminished in the presence of other ions; it then serving to carry a smaller fraction of the total current. Thus, if it is possible to add to the solution of M^+ a sufficient excess of another electrolyte whose cation does not show an electrochemical reaction until considerably more negative potentials than M^+, t_+ should become vanishingly small. The rate of arrival of M^+ at the cathode is then controlled solely by diffusion. Such an electrolyte is known as an *indifferent, base* or *supporting electrolyte*, potassium chloride being useful in this role and very commonly used. Thus, Equation (8.38) becomes

$$\frac{I_{\text{lim}}}{nF} = \frac{D[M]}{\delta} = \frac{i_{\text{lim}}}{SnF} \qquad (8.70)$$

S being the surface area of the electrode and i_{lim} the limiting diffusion-controlled *current*.

It is not easy to exploit the above equation directly as a basis for quantitative analysis, despite the simple proportionality between current and concentration. This is because reproducibility – a prime requirement in analysis is obtainable only with great difficulty with solid electrodes due to contamination by the products of electrolysis.

Polarography is based on the use of a dropping mercury electrode which consists of mercury in the form of small droplets issuing from the end of a fine-bore capillary. Despite the obvious slight practical complication of working with a dynamic rather than a static electrode, mercury in this form shows a number of distinct advantages over almost all other forms:

(1) The drops are reproducible so that the currents flowing, although varying with drop-growth and detachment from the capillary, are also reproducible.

(2) A fresh surface of electrode is continuously presented to the electrolyte solution thus almost eliminating chemical polarization effects.

(3) The hydrogen overvoltage for mercury as an electrode material is, as was seen in the last two sections, extremely high. It is therefore very rare for hydrogen evolution to interfere with the discharge of metal ions at a mercury electrode, particularly in solutions of high pH.

(4) The extent of electrolysis is small owing to the small electrode surface area, so that solutions may be electrolysed many times without measurable reduction in concentration.

The above advantages largely outweigh a few minor disadvantages, the most important of which are:

(1) The cathodic versatility of mercury is not matched by its anodic behaviour, mercury dissolution setting in at about 0.4 V (v saturated calomel electrode). Usually, as far as metal ions are concerned, this is of little importance, since almost all metal ions reduce at potentials considerably more negative than this.

(2) Oxygen is reduced by a two-stage process which shows a current–voltage curve extending over most of the cathodic working range. Dissolved oxygen must therefore be removed from a solution by flushing with some inert gas such as nitrogen, before electrolysis is attempted.

(3) Mercury is toxic, but sensible precautions make its use safe.

The basic circuit for polarography is shown in Fig. 8.12 and the shape of a

207

typical current-voltage curve is shown in Fig. 8.13. Such curves are generally known as *polarograms* or *polarographic waves.* The dotted line is that which would be obtained in the absence of reducible metal ion and only supporting electrolyte present. The final current rise is due to discharge of the supporting electrolyte cation, e.g. $K^+ + e \rightarrow K$ as an amalgam, while the so-called residual current is essentially a condenser or capacitance current due to the necessary charging of the mercury drops as the double layer is formed. This current may be described as non-faradaic in that its variation with potential is not governed by Ohm's law. It is seen that the residual current line cuts the voltage axis (usually at about -0.4 or 0.5 V *v.* S.C.E.) and corresponds to the electro-capillary zero (see Chapter 7) where the mercury carries no charge and the double layer, in effect, ceases to exist, the effect of the imposed potential being such that the natural charge which mercury adopts with respect to the aqueous solution is exactly neutralized. The increase of current due to both reduction of the metal ion under study and the supporting electrolyte cation occurs in accordance with Ohm's law and is described as faradaic.

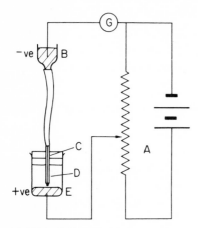

FIGURE 8.12
Basic polarographic circuit.

A. Potentiometer for variation of applied potential between C and E.
B. Mercury reservoir.
C. Dropping mercury electrode.
D. Working solution containing depolarizer(s) and supporting electrolyte.
E. Mercury pool anode: in precise measurements of potential this is replaced by a true reference electrode
such as a saturated calomel electrode.

The current plateau corresponds to the condition that the metal ions are reduced as fast as they reach the electrode by natural diffusion – a condition of complete concentration polarization. Reducible and oxidizable species which show such polarographic characteristics are often referred to as *depolarizers*. Reference to the polarogram will make such terminology clear. An electrode may be experimentally recognized as being polarized when its potential may be altered at will without any appreciable change in current flow being observed. This is seen to be the condition at the foot and plateau of the polarogram. On the rising part of the wave, however, this is not the case and the electrode becomes depolarized by (in this case) the reduction process.

8.7.1 Characteristics of diffusion-controlled polarographic waves

The magnitude of diffusion-controlled currents are direct functions of depolarizer concentration and in this fact lies the quantitative analytical significance of polarography. All quantitative analysis by the technique is based on the direct proportionality between the limiting diffusion controlled current and

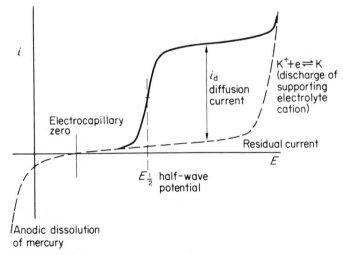

FIGURE 8.13
Essential features of a polarographic current–voltage curve, wave or polarogram. The dotted curve is that obtained with supporting electrolyte only, the final current rise corresponding to discharge of its cation. The polarogram corresponding to reduction of a depolarizer is superimposed on this supporting electrolyte curve.

209

depolarizer concentration as expressed in the Ilkovic equation viz.,

$$i_d = 706nD^{1/2}m^{2/3}t^{1/6}C \tag{8.71}$$

Here, n is the number of electrons exchanged in the electrode reaction, D is the diffusion coefficient of the depolarizer ($cm^2\ s^{-1}$), m is the rate of mass flow of the mercury ($mg\ s^{-1}$), t is the drop time (s) and C is the depolarizer concentration. With the last quantity expressed as millimole litre^{-1}, and the numerical constant 706, the *maximum* current during the drop-life is given in microamps. If, as is more usual, mean currents are measured, the numerical constant becomes 607, and the practical form of the Ilkovic equation becomes

$$\bar{i}_d = 607nD^{1/2}m^{2/3}t^{1/6}C \tag{8.72}$$

The potential at the mid-point of the wave where $i = i_d/2$, is known as the half-wave potential, $E_{1/2}$, and this quantity is characteristic of a given depolarizer for fixed solution and environmental conditions. As such, half-wave potentials may be used to identify qualitatively components in a mixture of depolarizers. Values are, however, extremely sensitive to the presence of different complexing species, including supporting electrolyte anions, and $E_{1/2}$ values should be used for 'fingerprinting' only with extreme caution. Provided that the reduction process occurs reversibly the currents and corresponding potentials on the rising portions of waves are related through the Heyrovsky–Ilkovic equation

$$E = E_{1/2} + \frac{RT}{nF} \ln \frac{\bar{i}_d - \bar{i}}{\bar{i}} \tag{8.73}$$

Equation (8.73) is seen to be very similar to the Nernst equation and may be regarded as its polarographic equivalent, $E_{1/2}$ replacing $E^{\ominus}$, to which it closely corresponds in magnitude. A plot of $\ln\{\bar{i}_d - \bar{i}/\bar{i}\}$ versus E may be used to determine both n and an accurate value of $E_{1/2}$ (Fig. 8.14).

For irreversible reductions, a wave has less than the theoretical slope for the number of electrons transferred and Equation (8.73) must be modified to

$$E = E_{1/2} + \frac{RT}{\alpha nF} \ln \frac{\bar{i}_d - \bar{i}}{\bar{i}} \tag{8.74}$$

α being the transfer coefficient. It is instructive to compare the expected

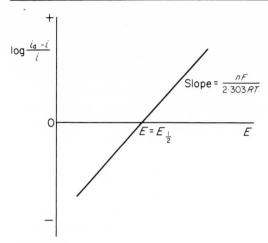

FIGURE 8.14
Logarithmic analysis of a reversible polarographic wave.

shapes for two reductions having the same n value, one involving a rapid electron transfer (reversible), the other a slow one (irreversible) as shown in Fig. 8.15.

For wave 1, diffusion is rate-determining over the entire wave profile, the mass transfer process being always slower than the electron-exchange rate provided, of course, that the reduction potential of the depolarizer has been reached. For wave 2, the electron transfer process is rate-determining over

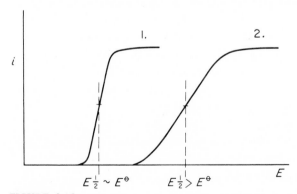

FIGURE 8.15
Comparison of polarograms for (1) a reversible, and (2) an irreversible reduction; the limiting currents in both cases being diffusion controlled and the number of electrons transferred equal.

211

lower parts of the wave, even these small currents requiring large (activation) overvoltage to sustain them. It is not until the later part of the wave, where even more overvoltage is applied, that the electron transfer rate becomes of such a magnitude that this process gives way to the diffusion process in determining the rate. Thus, it is important to realize that, even for such slow processes, the *limiting* currents are subject to diffusion control and as such are given by the Ilkovic equation. It follows that both reversible and irreversible diffusion controlled waves may be exploited analytically. For analysis it is possible to draw a calibration graph of diffusion current versus concentration and to read 'unknown' concentrations from this. Sometimes it may be more convenient to employ standard addition techniques, whereby the increase in a current signal caused by the addition of a known concentration of the depolarizer to be determined, enables the concentration producing the original signal to be calculated by simple proportion.

In order to base analytical methods upon the application of the Ilkovic equation, it is essential to establish that limiting currents produced by depolarizers are diffusion controlled. This is by no means always the case. Rearrangement of Equation (8.73) in the form

$$\bar{i}_d = (607 n D^{1/2} C)(m^{2/3} t^{1/6})$$

emphasizes the presence of two types of variable in the Ilkovic equation – those concerned with the solution and those concerned with the electrode. When electrode factors are maintained constant, a linear relation between i_d and concentration is maintained. If solution factors are maintained constant, $i_d \propto m^{2/3} t^{1/6}$. By Poiseuille's equation, the rate of flow of a liquid (v) through a capillary under a head of liquid is directly proportional to the height of the column, h. Therefore $v \propto m \propto h$, and since also $v \propto 1/t$, $i_d \propto h^{2/3} h^{-1/6} = h^{1/2}$. Thus, a diffusion-controlled wave shows a linear relationship between i_d and the square root of the height of the mercury reservoir.

The simplest experimental arrangement may be used for concentration determinations in the range $10^{-5} M$ to $10^{-2} M$. Below about $10^{-4} M$, however, the ratio of faradaic current to the concentration-independent non-faradaic capacitance current, becomes progressively smaller until the latter predominates. All modern instrumental refinements, whose discussion is beyond the scope of this book, are aimed at improving this ratio.

212

8.7.2 *Other types of polarographic wave*

Some depolarizers are observed to produce waves which are smaller than those predicted by the Ilkovic equation and whose heights show no variation with h. These waves are controlled by the rate of some chemical reaction preceding the electron transfer. A good example of such a system is provided by the behaviour of formaldehyde. This compound exists in aqueous solution largely as the hydrate which is electro-inactive and produces no reduction wave. The anhydrous molecule, which is reducible is formed from the hydrate only slowly. The overall reaction may be represented by

$$(HO)_2CH_2 \underset{k_{-1}}{\overset{k_1}{\rightleftharpoons}} H_2O + CH_2O \xrightarrow{2H^+ + 2e} CH_3OH \qquad (8.76)$$

Sometimes, currents may be found which are many times larger than would be expected for a diffusion-controlled process. These are found when a species is reduced at the dropping electrode to form a product which rapidly reacts chemically with some other species in the solution to regenerate the original depolarizer. Such behaviour is shown by ferric species in the presence of hydrogen peroxide, the reaction scheme being simply

$$\begin{array}{c} Fe^{3+} + e \rightarrow Fe^{2+} \\ \uparrow \underline{\qquad\qquad\qquad} \\ H_2O_2 \end{array} \qquad (8.77)$$

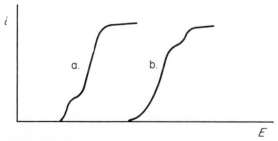

FIGURE 8.16
Superposition upon normal waves of pre- and post-adsorption waves.

(a) The product of the reduction process is adsorbed on the electrode surface and not produced in the free state.

(b) The oxidized form is adsorbed; adsorption forces must be overcome during the formation of the product, a process requiring a more negative potential.

213

A further type of wave, whose height is a direct linear function of h, is characteristic of adsorption processes at the dropping mercury electrode. An adsorption wave is always associated with a larger wave and occurs either just prior to or just after the latter (Fig. 8.16). So-called pre-waves are caused by the product of a reduction process becoming adsorbed at the drop surface, this requiring less energy owing to it not being necessary to produce the free product. Post-waves correspond to adsorption of the oxidized form and have more negative half-wave potentials, owing to the necessity of overcoming adsorption forces during the formation of products.

8.8   Mixed potentials and double electrodes

The potential adopted by a metal in aqueous solution is not always governed by the M^{n+}/M equilibrium which might be expected for simple cases. Other reactions may occur when the metal is thermodynamically unstable in aqueous solution. In particular, the reduction of hydrogen ions may interfere with the electrode equilibrium. Consider a metal such as zinc, with a fairly negative electrode potential, in an acidic solution containing its cations. If more positive potentials were to be imposed upon the zinc electrode the current density would vary according to the Tafel line as the metal ionized (assuming only activation polarization) (Fig. 8.17).

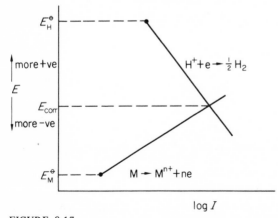

FIGURE 8.17

Mixed or corrosion potential in acid solution for a metal with an electrode potential which is negative relative to hydrogen.

The standard potential of hydrogen is considerably more positive than that of zinc, but at potentials more negative than $E_H^\ominus$, the rate of hydrogen discharge increases according to its characteristic Tafel line. At the point where the two Tafel lines meet, both reactions must occur at the same current density, so that the potential corresponding to this intersection point is a steady one which is known as a *mixed* or *corrosion* potential. The situation may alternatively be represented by the current–potential relationships for the two reactions (Fig. 8.18).

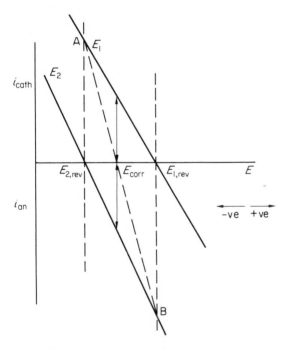

FIGURE 8.18
Resultant current–potential plot (A–B) for a mixed electrode. At the corrosion potential equal currents flow in opposite directions.

The actual potential adopted by the system for different currents will follow the resultant line AB which at $E = E_{corr}$ gives equal currents flowing in opposite directions. The species co-reducing need not be hydrogen but may be any species reducing at a more positive potential than M^{n+}.

8.8.1 Corrosion processes and Pourbaix diagrams

Graphs of reversible metal electrode potentials versus pH of solutions into which they dip at fixed temperature and pressure, provide important information regarding the thermodynamic stability of various phases. Such Pourbaix diagrams provide a *thermodynamic* basis for the explanation of corrosion reactions. It must, however, be emphasized that the construction of such diagrams takes no account of the kinetics of reactions which occur under the conditions represented by various areas appearing on them. This means that they should be used with some caution when attempting to *predict* corrosion behaviour. A much simplified Pourbaix diagram for iron in aqueous solution is shown in Fig. 8.19. Here the dotted lines labelled a and b give the pH dependence of the equilibrium potentials of hydrogen and oxygen electrodes. The area labelled 'passivation' corresponds to the formation of solid compound on the metal surface which protects the metal from attack.

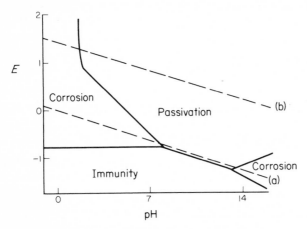

FIGURE 8.19
Simplified Pourbaix diagram for the iron–water system. a, b are the pH dependences of E_{eq} for hydrogen and oxygen electrodes respectively.

High hydrogen overvoltages prevent high-purity metals from corroding at anything but very slow rates. In the presence of more noble metal impurities, however, corrosion rates may become greatly accelerated, the more noble metal regions acting as 'local cathodes' at which hydrogen evolution may take place.

In neutral and alkaline solutions, the mixed potential attained is usually insufficient to cause hydrogen evolution, at least at atmospheric pressure. In such cases oxygen, either adsorbed at the surface or in solution, may itself become a depolarizer undergoing reduction by the following cathodic processes.

$$O_2 + 2\,H_2O + 4\,e \rightarrow 4\,OH^- \tag{8.78a}$$

and

$$O_2 + 4\,H_3O^+ + 4\,e \rightarrow 6\,H_2O \tag{8.78b}$$

Such *partial* cathodic processes may well occur via adsorbed oxygen or oxides. Areas where oxide or oxygen are *not* adsorbed then correspond to anodes, and in this way *local cells* may be set up over the whole of the metal surface.

Corrosion rates involving oxygen consumption vary in a quite different manner to those involving hydrogen evolution. While the latter type starts very slowly, even in the presence of noble metal impurities, increasing dissolution exposes increasing areas of noble metal, to form an increasing number of local cathodes. The rate then accelerates rapidly. In corrosion involving oxygen, initial rates are high and drop to low steady values very rapidly; the rapid decline corresponding to the removal of adsorbed oxygen, after which the corrosion rate becomes largely dependent on the rate of diffusion of oxygen to the metal surface. In the rusting of iron, for instance, the initial reactions appear to be dissolution of iron to give ferrous ions at local anodes. These ferrous ions then combine with hydroxyl ions, formed at local cathodes, to produce ferrous hydroxide. If sufficient oxygen is available, the ferrous hydroxide may be oxidized to rust, $Fe_2O_3 . H_2O$. In practice the products of intermediate oxidation stages (Fe_3O_4 and hydrates) also occur due to lack of oxygen. Corroded surfaces show formation of these products in preferential layers, the true rust deposit being outermost.

The above reactions are not observed with metals which form an oxide surface layer in air, except in the neighbourhood of cracks or large pores in the layer. At such points anodic dissolution may occur. In cases where the anodically formed ions produce oxide after reacting with hydroxyl ions formed at a local cathode, the fault in the protective film becomes sealed against further corrosion. Should different products be formed, the development of further local cells is encouraged and severe local corrosion may result.

217

8.8.2 *Corrosion prevention*

Corrosion reactions may be minimized by essentially two means. Firstly, by covering the surfaces of metals with protective films and secondly, by exploiting inhibition processes. Steel, for example, may be protected by surface layers of chromium, nickel, zinc or tin. Cracks in a surface film of a more noble metal than the one being offered protection, can give rise to local cells in which the exposed base metal becomes an anode and the protective layer a cathode. Local corrosion then sets in.

On the other hand, if the protective layer is of a less noble metal, the base material becomes cathodic in any region where there is a crack or fault, favouring metal deposition. This constitutes what has become known as 'cathodic protection' and is employed extensively in the protection from corrosion of metals in marine use.

Oxide layers formed by some metals in the atmosphere are most useful if they are physically tough and damage resistant. In any case, if damage should occur, the protective layer rapidly reforms. Thicker coatings may be obtained by anodizing, i.e. by anodically polarizing the material by electrolysis with some cathode in a suitable electrolyte.

Inhibiting reactions form an important part of corrosion prevention. Any material which inhibits, either partially or completely, the initial reaction at local anodes and cathodes comes within this category. Anodic inhibitors are species which can complex with anodically formed metal ions to produce protective layers. It is, however, vital that such species should be present in sufficient concentration to give protection at *all* local anodes, otherwise corrosion at a relatively few unprotected sites will cause extreme damage. Cathodic inhibitors increase the discharge overvoltage of hydrogen ions or prevent the formation of molecular hydrogen from atoms.

8.9   Electrochemical processes as sources of energy

Electrical energy may be produced through the operation of a chemical reaction taking place in a galvanic cell. The earliest, most rudimentary form of galvanic cell consisted of alternate sheets of copper and zinc separated by wet cloth. This arrangement subsequently gave rise, in a rather different form, to the Daniell cell.

Since one cannot normally expect to obtain reactions giving a free energy change of more than about 200 kJ per faraday, application of $\Delta G = -nEF$ leads to the conclusion that about 2 V is the maximum e.m.f. obtainable from a simple cell. Higher voltages may, of course, be produced through appropriate banking of large numbers of cells.

There are essentially three types of galvanic cell, viz.:

(i) Primary cells

These are based upon reactions which are not reversible so that recharging is out of the question and once the cell reaction has proceeded to completion, the cell is discarded.

(ii) Accumulators or storage batteries

Such cells are based upon almost reversible electrode processes. All processes occurring during their discharge while used as a source of e.m.f. may to a large extent be reversed in the recharging process. The overall efficiency of the recharging reaction may be significantly reduced by side reactions.

(iii) Fuel cells

In fuel cells an attempt is made to make the fullest possible use of the free energy of reactions, such as the combustion of fuels, to produce electrical energy. Processes are chosen which occur as nearly reversible as possible in order to obtain the maximum useful proportion of ΔG. The mode of operation of fuel cells is fundamentally different from that of batteries. While batteries *store* electrical energy, fuel cells convert energy obtainable from chemical processes *directly* into electricity.

It is not possible with conventional cells to make full use of the maximum (reversible) work which is, in principle, derivable from the reactions upon which they operate. The maximum e.m.f., to which this maximum work corresponds is only obtained when the reaction occurs strictly reversibly at the condition of zero current flow. For a measurable current flow only a fraction of the maximum work may be exploited. Even so, the fraction of ΔG usable may be of the order of 80–90% which compares very favourably with that obtained for combustion fuel engines which is not more than 35%.

8.9.1 Primary cells

As an example of this type we may consider the Leclanché cell, which is represented as follows

$$Zn \mid NH_4Cl \ (20\%), \ ZnCl_2 \mid MnO_2, \ C \qquad (8.79)$$

(formed into a gel by the
addition of starch)

Such 'dry cells', with the electrolyte medium so thickened by the use of suitable additives, may be used in any position without spillage. The reactions occurring in the cell are complex but the behaviour of the system may be largely explained in terms of the following:

At the anode (−ve)

$$Zn \rightarrow Zn^{2+} + 2 \ e \qquad (E^{\ominus} = -0.76 \ V) \qquad (8.80)$$

At the cathode (+ve)

$$MnO_2 + H_3O^+ + e \rightarrow MnOOH$$

followed by

$$2 \ MnOOH \rightarrow Mn_2O_3 + H_2O \qquad (8.81)$$

Evolution of hydrogen gas at the cathode would be most undesirable and, in any case, would cause serious losses of energy. It is to prevent such an occurrence that the cathode is surrounded by manganese dioxide (the depolarizer), which discourages hydrogen formation by undergoing other reactions preferentially. The manganese dioxide proves to be more efficient in this respect when it contains lattice defects which may be artificially induced.

The Leclanché cell is irreversible, and therefore incapable of recharging, because of the occurrence of side reactions such as

$$OH^- + NH_4^+ \rightarrow H_2O + NH_3$$

$$2 \ NH_3 + Zn^{2+} + 2 \ Cl^- \rightarrow Zn(NH_3)_2Cl_2$$

(a sparingly soluble
complex which forms
a crystalline deposit)

$$Zn^{2+} + 2 \ OH^- \rightarrow ZnO + H_2O \qquad (8.82)$$

The cell provides a cheap source of electrical energy with an e.m.f. of about 1·6 V, but since the cathode potential is a function of pH, this value falls rapidly on continuous discharge.

A more constant voltage is produced by the Ruben–Mallory cell in which a large excess of hydroxyl ions renders its operation less sensitive to pH change. This cell usually takes the form

$$Hg \mid HgO, KOH, Zn(OH)_2 \mid Zn \qquad (8.83)$$

Air or oxygen cells are modifications of the Leclanché cell in that the cathode is activated carbon in contact with atmospheric oxygen. Two forms are

$$Zn \mid NH_4Cl \mid C(O_2)$$

or

$$Zn \mid NaOH \mid C(O_2) \qquad (8.84)$$

Such cells give a maximum e.m.f. of about 1·5 V and have satisfactory voltage-time characteristics. Their major disadvantage is that they cannot be highly loaded due to the slow rate of oxygen polarization so that they operate most satisfactorily for very low currents or in intermittant use.

8.9.2 Storage batteries

The lead accumulator is an example of a galvanic cell in which electrode processes are almost reversible. The action is based upon the pre-electrolysis of a solution of sulphuric acid saturated with lead sulphate between lead electrodes. Lead is deposited at the cathode, while plumbous ions are oxidized to the plumbic state at the anode. The Pb^{4+} ions are subsequently hydrolysed and deposited as PbO_2. In practice the electrodes are usually in the form of grids of a lead/antimony alloy (for mechanical strength) filled with a paste of red lead and litharge in sulphuric acid. As initially constructed, therefore, the system corresponds to the situation existing in the fully discharged cell. On electrolysis the anode forms porous PbO_2 while the cathode forms spongy lead. This charging process, together with the reverse discharge reaction, may be written overall as

$$2\,PbSO_4 + 2\,H_2O \underset{\text{discharging}}{\overset{\text{charging}}{\rightleftarrows}} PbO_2 + Pb + 2\,H_2SO_4 \qquad (8.85)$$

During the *discharge* process, in which the cell acts spontaneously, the following reactions occur;

At the lead electrode

$$Pb + SO_4^{2-} \rightarrow PbSO_4 + 2\,e \qquad (8.86)$$

At the PbO_2 electrode

$$PbO_2 + 4\,H^+ \rightarrow Pb^{4+} + 2\,H_2O \qquad (i)$$

$$Pb^{4+} + 2\,e \rightarrow Pb^{2+} \qquad (ii)$$

$$Pb^{2+} + SO_4^{2-} \rightarrow PbSO_4 \qquad (iii)$$

overall

$$PbO_2 + 4\,H^+ + SO_4^{2-} + 2\,e \rightarrow PbSO_4 + 2\,H_2O \qquad (8.87)$$

During the charging process, these reactions are reserved.

The potential of the PbO_2 electrode, from a consideration of the electrochemical step (ii), is given by

$$E_{PbO_2} = E_{Pb^{4+}/Pb^{2+}}^{\ominus} + \frac{RT}{2F} \ln \frac{a_{Pb^{4+}}}{a_{Pb^{2+}}} \qquad (8.88)$$

but, since $a_{Pb^{4+}} \sim a_{Pb^{2+}}$, and both are very small since the solution is saturated with PbO_2 and $PbSO_4$,

$$E \sim E_{Pb^{4+}/Pb^{2+}}^{\ominus} \sim +1 \cdot 70 \text{ V}$$

The potential of the lead electrode is given by

$$E_{Pb} = E_{Pb^{2+}/Pb}^{\ominus} + \frac{RT}{2F} \ln a_{Pb^{2+}} \sim -0 \cdot 28 \text{ V} \qquad (8.89)$$

Therefore, the cell e.m.f. $\sim 1 \cdot 70 - (-0 \cdot 28) = +1 \cdot 98$ V.

Charging and discharging curves for a lead accumulator are shown in Fig. 8.20, from which it is evident that the processes are not completely reversible. Mixed potentials occurring at the electrodes cause them to corrode and give rise to 'spontaneous discharge', so that, even when no current is being drawn from the cell, the following (irreversible) reactions occur.

At the Pb electrode

$$Pb + 2\,H^+ \rightarrow Pb^{2+} + H_2 \qquad (8.90)$$

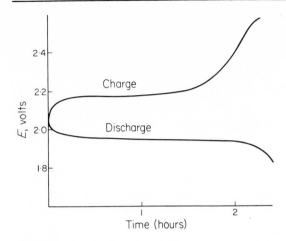

FIGURE 8.20
Constant current charging/discharging curves for a lead accumulator.

Consideration of this reaction stresses the importance of eliminating any metal which has a lower hydrogen overvoltage than lead. Even traces of such metals will poison the accumulator beyond repair.

At the PbO₂ electrode

$$PbO + Pb + 2\,H_2SO_4 \rightarrow 2\,PbSO_4 + 2\,H_2O \qquad (8.91)$$

This constitutes attack of the lead supporting the effective electrode material. The sulphate deposit from both this spontaneous discharge and from the normal discharge, coagulates with time and retards further electrode processes – an effect known as 'sulphation'. Regular charging can reduce such effects to a minimum.

The efficiency of such cells may be expressed in two ways.

(a) Current efficiency (E_i)
    This may be defined by

$$E_i = \frac{\text{charge produced while discharging}}{\text{charge taken up during charging}}$$

The product of i (amps) and time (hours) at any point on the charging or discharging curve of Fig. 8.20 gives the charge taken up or given out respectively in ampere hours. Thus,

$$\text{Current efficiency, } E_i = \frac{(it)_{\text{discharge}}}{(it)_{\text{charge}}} \tag{8.92}$$

which is about 95% for the lead accumulator.

(b) Energy efficiency (E_u)

This may be defined by

$$E_u = \frac{\text{energy given out during discharge}}{\text{energy taken up while charging}}$$

$$= \frac{E_{\text{discharge}} \times i \times t}{E_{\text{charge}} \times i \times t} \tag{8.93}$$

For the lead accumulator this ratio is about 0·8. The voltage obtainable during discharge will be less than the reversible value, E_{rev}, by overvoltage and iR corrections, thus

$$E_{\text{discharge}} = E_{\text{rev}} - \eta - iR \tag{8.94a}$$

η collecting both activation and concentration overvoltage effects. Conversely the voltage required for charging is in excess of E_{rev} according to

$$E_{\text{charge}} = E_{\text{rev}} - \eta' - iR \tag{8.94b}$$

η' again collecting overvoltages.

It is seen therefore that the current and energy efficiencies are related through the expression

$$E_u = \frac{E_{\text{dis}} - \eta - iR}{E_{\text{ch}} - \eta' - iR} \cdot E_i \tag{8.95}$$

Activation contributions to the overvoltage terms are small for this system, by far the larger part of both η and η' arising from concentration polarization effects. The two energies may be obtained from the areas under the respective curves, the difference between them being the energy loss.

Although the lead accumulator has high current and energy efficiencies, it leaves much to be desired when considered in the more important practical terms of its energy output to weight ratio. While improved output-to-weight ratios may be obtained by using larger surface area grid plates, these are less strong mechanically and current surges are liable to break up the delicate PbO_2 and $PbSO_4$ deposits to cause sludging. It is often more economical to use more durable electrode components at the expense of some efficiency.

In the Edison alkaline accumulator, a 20% solution of potassium hydroxide is electrolysed between a cathode of iron/ferrous hydroxide and an anode of nickel hydroxide. These electrode materials are pressed into perforated steel containers along with mercury and finely divided nickel at cathode and anode respectively to raise the conductivity (which is low for hydroxides). During the charging process the following reactions occur.

At the Fe(OH)₂ electrode

$$Fe(OH)_2 + 2\,e \rightarrow Fe + 2\,OH^- \qquad (8.96)$$

At the Ni(OH)₂ electrode

$$Ni(OH)_2 + OH^- \rightarrow NiOOH + H_2O + e \qquad (8.97)$$

The overall charging/discharging reaction may therefore be written

$$2\,Ni(OH)_2 + Fe(OH)_2 \underset{\text{discharging}}{\overset{\text{charging}}{\rightleftarrows}} 2\,NiOOH + Fe + 2\,H_2O \qquad (8.98)$$

Side reactions such as

$$2\,NiOOH + Ni(OH)_2 \rightarrow Ni_3O_2(OH)_4$$

cause the process to be less reversible than those in the lead accumulator, the current efficiency being about 80% and the energy efficiency about 60%. The e.m.f. produced initially is close to the reversible value of 1·4 V, but drops rapidly to a fairly steady 1·3 V.

8.9.3   Fuel cells

The ideal efficiency, ϵ, of a fuel cell is given by

$$\epsilon = \frac{\Delta G}{\Delta H} = \frac{E}{E - T\left(\dfrac{\partial E}{\partial T}\right)_P} \qquad (8.99)$$

ΔH being the heat of the reaction used. This equation makes it clear that for a cell with a positive temperature coefficient, supply of external heating will, in principle, provide an efficiency greater than 100%.

The schematic arrangement of components in the Bacon hydrogen/oxygen fuel cell is shown in Fig. 8.21. Operation of the cell depends upon the following reactions

$$2\,H_2 \;\rightarrow\; 4\,H^+ + 4\,e$$

$$O_2 + 4\,H^+ + 4\,e \rightarrow 2\,H_2O$$

overall

$$2\,H_2 + O_2 \;\rightarrow\; 2\,H_2O; \qquad \Delta G^{\ominus} = 476{\cdot}3\ \text{kJ}$$

From the $\Delta G^{\ominus}$ value, it can be seen that the theoretical voltage is of the order of $1{\cdot}3$ V. In practice voltages of $1{\cdot}0{-}1{\cdot}1$ V are obtained.

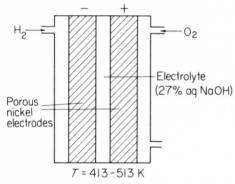

FIGURE 8.21
The Bacon fuel cell (schematic).

For an efficient cell all processes must occur rapidly. Reactants must be able to reach the electrodes easily so that porous electrodes with large internal surface areas, saturated with electrolyte, are used. The pore sizes are often graded from large on the gas side of an electrode to small on the electrolyte side. Good catalyst materials ensure rapid electrochemical reactions and, in combination with a higher temperature, help to suppress the cathodic formation of perhydroxyl ions by the reaction

$$O_2 + 2\,H_2O + 2\,e \rightarrow OH^- + OH_2^- \qquad (8.100)$$

With such precautions the hydrogen–oxygen cell can be made to show efficiencies of up to 75%. A Bacon-type cell has been successfully employed in space projects where the water produced – at the rate of about a pint per kilowatt hour – is used to supplement the water supply.

Many other fuel cell systems have been devised with varying degrees of success. Provided that certain inherent difficulties can be overcome, a wide variety of designs and modes of operation could become available for specific purposes. Their use for traction purposes to replace engines with high pollution risk is a major attraction. At the other extreme artificial hearts, powered by fuel cells consuming food fuels, have been suggested as a further possibility.

At present, a great drawback is that while the attractive prospect of the use of cheap fuels such as hydrocarbons presents itself, difficulties are encountered in practice by the poisoning of catalytic surfaces by intermediates.

Further Reading

Conway, B. E. (1965), *Theory and Principles of Electrode Processes*, Ronald Press, New York.

Crow, D. R. and Westwood, J. V. (1968), *Polarography*, Methuen, London.

Damaskin, B. B. (1967), *The Principles of Current Methods for the Study of Electrochemical Kinetics*, McGraw-Hill, New York.

Delahay, P. (1954), *New Instrumental Methods of Electrochemistry*, Interscience, New York.

Delahay, P. (1965), *Double Layer and Electrode Kinetics*, Wiley, New York.

Index